Lauren You're the boss!

BRAND *the* AUTHOR

(NOT THE BOOK)

KAREN A. CHASE

224PAGES
RICHMOND, VIRGINIA

224PAGES
P.O. Box 23259
Richmond, VA 23223
224Pages.com

★ ★ ★

Cover Design & Book Interior: 224Pages

★ ★ ★

BRAND THE AUTHOR (NOT THE BOOK)
A Workbook for Writing & Launching
Your Own Author Brand Plan

ISBN PRINT: 978-1-7337528-4-8
ISBN EBOOK: 978-1-7337528-5-5

To Katharine & Kris

For embracing writing goals, tacos,
chocolate, and Oxford commas.

Praise for the Workbook

"Mandatory reading for all new clients. Humorous and chock full of insightful tips.
This is a must-read for veteran authors and those who are just starting the journey.
Great advice from an expert in the field of marketing and branding.
You will find your copy dogeared, underlined, and flagged."

— Lisa Hagan, Literary Agent

"Karen has spent years doing classes and programs for James River Writers
and is one of our most popular instructors. I can't think of a better author to guide you
through the brand development process. Her workbook is accessible, insightful, and hilarious."

— Katharine Herndon, author and Executive Director of James River Writers

"Karen A. Chase shares her deep expertise in effectively reaching readers to lay out
not only the case for being mindful about our author brand, but also a set of concrete steps
toward defining and building one. Presented in an engaging and appealing workbook, the exercises
will gently guide anyone from an aspiring writer to a well-established career author, discovering
how best to present ourselves—and our books—to readers and the world. I wish that I'd had
this workbook when I was starting out—but I'm glad that I have it now!"

— Lars Hedbor, Author of *Tales from a Revolution Series*

"Conversational in tone, comprehensive in scope, *Brand the Author* is unparalleled in empowering
authors with clear steps to hone and commandeer their signature messages, services and reader
connections as author-entrepenuers. So wish I had this invaluable primer before publishing my
debut novel. The great news is I have it now. Authors: Do not just top your TBR pile with this
workbook, invest time in it and share it's empowering results with writers at every level."

— Robin Farmer, Author of *Malcolm and Me*

"This workbook is a MUST for all authors! Unlike other workbooks that merely outline a plan,
Karen provides a clear, comprehensive, actionable approach to being an *Author Entrepreneur*.
She makes the task of being your own boss attainable."

— E. Carson Williams, Author of *The Isle of Devils*

YOU'RE ABOUT TO EMBARK ON A JOURNEY
WHERE YOU WILL SOON STAND & SAY...

———

"I AM THE BOSS OF MY AUTHOR BUSINESS!"

———

Table of Contents

Know The Realities

It's not enough to write.
It's not enough to read.

We need to know the waters of the industry
we navigate if we are to captain our ships.

PART I
GETTING READY
Reframing our Roles

Should You Buy This Workbook?

This workbook is about branding for authors.

An author brand is your unique collection of fonts, colors, words, and imagery that are consistently applied to your platform tools to authentically to convey your message to your readers.

I can hear you already asking. "Do I really need a brand?" And if not, "Do I even need this workbook?"

Yes. And maybe. Workbooks are supposed to be helpful, and "help" can be best described through this joke:

How many therapists does it take to change a lightbulb?

One, but the lightbulb has to really want to change.

To be clear, this workbook won't provide clinical therapy for writers to "know thyself," as Socrates advises. (Although it's never a bad idea—self-knowledge improves character development, and this industry can be quite maddening at times.)

Rather, this workbook is designed as an inspiring step-by-step guide for how to create branded, effective platform tools to support your writing and publishing endeavors.

Regardless of where you are on that path, I encourage you to dive into this workbook for the right reasons. Then, you'll (happily) apply what you've learned. So, let's see... should you buy this workbook? Here's a simple two-part quiz:

Yes, authors really need an author brand plan!

YES, I WANT/NEED THIS WORKBOOK BECAUSE I...

- ❏ Am not sure what an author brand and platform tools are or why I need them.
- ❏ Do not have a written author brand and/or platform tools plan.
- ❏ Have been managing too many platform tools and tasks, so I need to simplify.
- ❏ Want to manage my communication with readers (and eventually attract more of them).
- ❏ Plan on writing (or have written) more than one book.
- ❏ Plan on publishing books (independently or with a publisher) as a career.
- ❏ Have never published a book, but I want to, so I need some foundational education.

NO, I DON'T NEED THIS BOOK BECAUSE I...

- ❏ Want to write only one book and it's primarily for my family.
- ❏ Have a good author brand/tools plan and only need specific book marketing advice.*
- ❏ Firmly believe magic fairies (publishers) will take care of my brand and tools for I...
  - am the next Elizabeth Gilbert or Lee Child whom Oprah has yet to discover.**
  - prefer to be left alone to write and drink with six-toed cats in Cuba because that's what Hemingway did and look how famous he became!***
  - I am so busy I've never finished a project or story (nor the dishes piled in my sink.)****

If you checked any of the NO comments, please read the footnotes, and you'll see this is likely not the workbook for you.

If you checked any or all of the YES comments, though, it is for you, so let's get started. (This workbook equals the cost of a nice lunch and a latte. By comparison, hiring a professional to help you with a brand plan can run you about $1000, so what do you have to lose?)

* This workbook isn't about the nuts and bolts of using social media, running ads on Amazon, or promoting your books across all your platform tools without irritating your readers. That said, you might learn a thing or two about how to improve the effectiveness of those tools as you build your brand.

** Even super-published greats like Elizabeth Gilbert expertly manage their author brand and platform tools. She may not personally manage it all, but she hires and directs those who do. She's the expert so she is writing and presenting TedTalks and podcasts. True, she has more money than you might have, but earning more in publishing absolutely results in having more details to manage. Be careful what you wish for, my dear author.

*** Famous but drunk and miserable and sadly suffering with PTSD from his war-correspondent days. Be careful what you wish for, my dear author.

**** Branding and marketing yourself means MORE projects, so maybe this isn't the right time for you to go on this journey. Instead, please go wash those dishes. There's a lot of bacteria in your kitchen sink, and it's making me itchy.

How to Use This Workbook

Do you want to write and publish for many years to come? If so, take your time working through these sections to build a better foundation for your impending and illustrious career. Terms and advice are included throughout.

At the end of each of the main workbook sections, you'll find a **Summary of Decisions** space. Transferring your final answers to the **Summary of Decisions** space before you move on to the next section is necessary because later sections rely on your commitments in earlier sections.

I suggest you work in 90-minute bursts with 15-minute breaks. **Section 1: Get Yourself Organized** will help you determine how many hours each week you can allocate to this plan. Look for **Tidbits** for extra knowledge and inspiration.

Above all, be kind to yourself as you enjoy learning more about what makes you a unique, desirable author for your targeted readers.

Follow these steps in this order:

Step One

Read Part I and skim through the whole workbook without doing any of the work yet.

Step Two

Turn back to SECTION 1: GET YOURSELF ORGANIZED and begin working.

Step Three

Write. Answers. Down. This is about creating a written plan you'll follow and share.

Step Four

At the end of each section fill in your SUMMARY OF DECISIONS.

Step Five

Repeat steps two to four for all six sections.

Step Six

Read through the POST-BRAND PLANNING section and enact your plan.

Tidbit WHY WORK IN 90-MINUTE BURSTS?

Called the *ultradian rhythm*, 90-minute bursts are the optimum time your brain is capable of working on a single project. Beyond the 90 minutes, you get an adrenaline rush, and your cortisol levels rise (which contributes to dementia). Plus, chances are your work isn't as good as it could be, because you're not as productive after an hour and a half has gone by.

In a 2013 Forbes article, Tony Schwartz, author of *The Power of Full Engagement* said, "For my first three books, I sat at my desk for up to 10 hours a day. Each of the books took me at least a year to write. For my two most recent books, I wrote in three uninterrupted 90-minute sessions … Writing just four and half hours a day, I completed both books in less than six months." Whoa.

Tidbit BELIEVE IN ANALYSIS & DECISIONS

A few years ago, I worked with an author who was eager to develop her own brand. She wanted to jump in and design a new logo and make social media posts without examining her goals and capabilities. She also second-guessed every decision she made about her brand messaging and audience. She didn't examine her business options and wasn't decisive. Consequently, her work stalled and she still has no discernible brand.

How do you avoid this problem? You apply these two pieces of advice about *analysis* and *decision* from Bill Marriott:

"In business, information is extremely important, and so is analysis. I don't believe in analysis by paralysis, but… analysis is the key to making good decisions."

"Once you decide to decide, life becomes very simple. You don't have to think about certain issues or questions again. You simply get on with things and don't waste time and energy rehashing—debating and arguing—the problems and possibilities."

J.W. "Bill" Marriott is the founder of Marriott International, Inc., one of the world's largest lodging companies. Applying this advice saved me (and will save you) a ton of hand-wringing time that's better used for writing. For more advice from Bill, check out this blog link: bit.ly/KAC_BrandAuthor1

Why This Workbook is Necessary

Publishing has changed.

Let me repeat. *Publishing. Has. Changed.*

In 2009, Amazon Publishing emerged. In 2013, the six big international publishers became "The Big Five" when Penguin and Random House merged. In that same year, 416,438 books were indie-published and by 2018 the number eclipsed 1.6 million.*

When I refer to "indie-published," I mean those authors who are managing the bulk of the costs and publication responsibilities. "Indie-published" doubles for the phrase "self-published," but it does not include paying to publish with a hybrid press. (More on that later.)

When we couple relatively recent, massive industry changes with advances in technology—production of audio books, ebooks, ibooks, plus print-on-demand, uploading, shipping, tracking, etc.—we get an industry that not only has changed, it is changing. *Constantly.*

Unfortunately, despite working in an industry where change is resulting in more opportunities to be published, many authors (even those who have published half a dozen books) are still clinging to outdated beliefs about authorship. I list four of them here.

Outdated Belief No. 1:
The only successful author path is traditional publishing.

Agent, then editor, then traditional publisher. That's how the path goes, right? (Oh—like it's 1950 and you must get engaged, then married, then buy a house, then have kids… It's called "traditional" for a reason, which isn't always "right" for everyone, honey.)

The traditional path is *not* the only one. Sadly, many agents, publishers, writing conferences, and magazine articles still drill this misconception into authors and aspiring authors. Success, they say, equals being traditionally published. To indie-publish is a last resort, and only if you fail at the traditional route.

No. Stop it. Don't believe it.

Publishing just ain't what it used to be, baby, but there are many paths to a successful publishing career—soooo many and soooo varied.

If you're a professor, poet, or museum director, an academic press might publish your books, and you'll by-pass the agent altogether. You could indie-publish only, like Hugh Howey, bestselling author of *Wool* and other books, and make a fabulous living. (The man lives on a boat in the islands!) You could indie-publish and get a movie deal like Andy Weir with *The Martian*. You could freelance-write, indie-publish a few books, secure speaking engagements, or apply for fellowships, and be successful while never entering the traditional sphere at all.

Today, there isn't just one path.

* Bowker's self-publishing report: bit.ly/KAC_BrandAuthor2

Success is not tied to the route itself. However, having a written plan to support your author life that deepens and broadens your publishing options can improve the likelihood of long-term success.

Outdated Belief No. 2: Publishers and agents handle marketing.

I had that daydream you're having. Major book deal, six-figure advances, cocktails in the afternoon, and being left alone to write for months on end—except when your publicist gets you an interview on *The Late Late Show*. (For the record, host James Corden doesn't know I exist, and I think he's missing out.) However, that daydream is just… a dream. Because it is not 1950. It's not even 2005!

Back then, publishers used to put out fewer books per year at a pace that allowed for more marketing of those select books. At that time, there were also fewer marketing outlets.

Today, it takes for-freaking-ever for a book to get traditionally published. It's typically eighteen months or more once the ink finally dries on the publishing contract. And that takes time, too.

Today, the average traditional advance is smaller than it was two decades ago, plus your book is one of thousands hitting the shelves each month (along with thousands of indie-published books). Having more books in circulation means most publishers are spending less time marketing each book.

Tidbit READERS ARE WHAT WE'RE AFTER

Seth Godin, a marketing guru worth reading and hearing, suggests authors leave traditional publishing behind along with its debilitating rejection system. Moreover, he says to stop aspiring to get on (as he calls it), "the stupid *New York Times Best Seller List.*"

Instead, ask these questions.

"How few people can I influence and still be able to do this tomorrow?"

"How many readers do I need to connect with, and in what way, in order to finance my writing life?"

I suggest listening to a splendid interview with Seth Godin on the Podcast *On Being*. His insights will help support the work you'll do in this workbook. Listen here: bit.ly/KAC_BrandAuthor3

Even with a good contract, publishers typically invest in marketing and PR for three to six months—and not all books are treated equally. After that, efforts trickle to a mere drip. With dozens of social channels and marketing tools to manage, publishers are not going to wade into ongoing marketing for all of their authors. Why?

Authors and publishers are not selling the same thing.

What?! But aren't authors and publishers both selling books? That leads us to…

Outdated Belief No. 3: Publishers and authors both sell books.

Remember Meg Ryan's line as Kathleen Kelly in the hit movie *You've Got Mail*? "I have met Joe Fox. And I have heard him compare his store to a Price Club and the books in it to cans of olive oil."

True, Kathleen Kelly was referring to big-box bookstores; however, publishers today are more like Joe Fox than Kathleen Kelly.

In business, you're selling either a product or a service.

Publishers sell a product.

In order to meet their overhead and improve their bottom line, they need to move the commodity they sell (books), and the more the merrier. At times, the quality doesn't even matter.

I'm not saying publishers can't be altruistic. Some publishers have a sincere mission to bring thoughtful, well-written books to market. But even their mission is realized through high sales numbers and higher bottom lines. Their profits are tied to moving books by the truckload.

Yours is, too, you say? Not quite…

Your story is a collection of words you craft for a specific result. While that book might seem like a product, what you provide is actually a service to readers—whether that's escape, instruction, entertainment, inspiration, or understanding. As a result, your livelihood is tied to the *feeling* you ignite in your reader.

Authors sell an experience.

And that experience is not realized through book sales alone. Connecting with your reader begins or deepens through speaking engagements, published articles, classroom visits, and more. But that reader-by-reader experience is the business of the author, not the publisher.

Because of that, publishers expect (and in some ways have abandoned) authors to carry the bulk of the reader-connection business. It's a ton of responsibility. And work. Which means providing that service is a business. *Your* business.

Considering you're the one creating the reader experience (writing) AND increasing the reader engagement (connections), how you are marketing that service needs to be easy and smart. Plus, you can't spend money willy nilly. Which is why you need a plan. Which is why you must let go of…

Outdated Belief No. 4:
Authors spend their time writing.

As I've been building brands for authors—whether they've published one book or twenty—they come to me with sorrowful stories of low sales and meager reader connections.

Without fail, each author has spent the majority (if not all) of their time on improving the craft of writing. This grave error is best understood through a wine analogy.

Pour yourself a glass of Chardonnay and read on...

To focus only on improving your writing skills is akin to a vintner focused solely on the craft of making a better wine. If vintners spent all their time making the perfect barrel of Chardonnay with no investment in bottling it, creating a tasting room, or with no understanding about who would buy and drink the stuff, you'd be holding an empty glass in your hand.

*A cellar full of barrels
does not a vintner make.
What a terrible waste of grapes.*

*A shelf of books with no one
to read them does not
an author make.
What a terrible waste of trees.*

Authors who do not learn how to package and promote themselves so they can engage with readers might have their books read by their mothers and a few friends (some of whom claimed they read it). This is especially true for indie authors.

Authors want and need readers, so what's the solution to learning how to get your book (wine) to readers so they can experience it? By reframing how you see yourself. You're no longer an author. You must become an *Author Entrepreneur*.

Tidbit WHO DO READERS REMEMBER?

Are authors more important to readers than publishers? Take this quiz:

★ Name your favorite book.
★ Name the author of that book.
★ Did you seek other titles from that author?
★ Now, without peeking, who published that author's books?
★ Did you seek other titles from that publisher as a result of that one book?

I think you know the outcome here.

You're an Author Entrepreneur

All the authors I've ever worked with—no matter where they were in their career or how they were published—admitted they felt disappointed by that career. Many suffered from a lack of confidence.

A root cause for this disappointment is an industry that requires authors to spend so much time seeking, or waiting for, the approval of others. Agents, publishers, editors, booksellers, queries, submissions, and rejections... good heavens! *So. Many. Rejections.* It all makes us feel utterly powerless—but we aren't.

How can authors take back their power?

By managing the business of being an author—fully owning it. It's at that point you can call yourself an *Author Entrepreneur.* And as you learn to manage your career, you'll elevate your position.

You must become the boss of you!

When you do, all those people you assumed were gatekeepers are instead potential partners and vendors. They are in the roles of supporting *your* business, not the other way around. Therefore, it becomes necessary to evaluate them just as you would employees. You're giving them a portion of your profits. What are they doing to earn it?

If an agent offers to represent you, do they actually get back to you in a timely manner? Do they have publishing data? Do they have a track record that shows they're worth 15% of your business?

Which of your favorite booksellers will help your business connect with your readers the most? Do they have programs and events that historically bring in readers to support local or genre-specific authors?

If a traditional publisher contracts with you to get 90% of your gross profits (yes, 90!!), what distribution services or connections does it provide that you don't have? If they don't have distribution, can you pay an independent sales rep less to do more?

While it means more work to be sure, being an *Author Entrepreneur* is empowering. *You* decide who stays in your sphere and who goes.

If this sounds cold and impersonal, it's not. To again quote Kathleen Kelly in *You've Got Mail,* "Whatever else anything is, it ought to begin by being personal." Writing and publishing books is a business AND it is personal.

This book business begins and ends with your decisions because it begins and ends with your talents. You wrote the whole damn book. That makes the choices about this business—and the wonderful people you bring into it—yours.

The choices are entirely yours.

However, with power comes responsibility. To make wise choices you need to know where the money (earnings) comes from, so let's talk about money.

Download the graphic to the right (and others charts) from the workbook via: Bit.ly/KAC_BrandAuthor_BookFiles

REMEMBER YOUR ROLE.
YOU'RE NO LONGER ONLY AN AUTHOR.

———————

"I AM THE BOSS OF MY AUTHOR BUSINESS!"

———————

Copy this phrase and paste this phrase to your mirror. Each time you work on this workbook, first perform a simple exercise to remember you are an *Author Entrepreneur*. Stand tall before your mirror, feet firmly planted, arms akimbo, and say the above phrase aloud. No, I'm not joking. Trust me. This works to reinforce your power of decision making.

Post a video of the above on your favorite social feed.
I'll share it with my followers if you add:
#BossofMyAuthorBusiness
and tag me: @KarenAChase

Let's Talk About Money

We're told authors shouldn't talk about money. Traditional publishing contracts have long held confidentiality clauses. Indie-authors are afraid to talk about earnings because they assume the amount is less than traditional authors make. That's why we can't talk about money. It just ain't polite.

Watch out. Here comes a curse word. *Bullshit.*

Sure, there's some talk on Twitter and an occasional blog post, but we haven't been talking about what authors earn nearly enough. As a result, most authors (Suzanne Collins, Deepak Chopra, and Elisabeth Badinter aside) are typically making:
★ Less than we think
★ Less than readers think
★ Less than publishers/agents want us to believe
★ Less than we could

Proof? According to a 2019 New York Times article entitled *Does it Pay to Be a Writer* by Concepción de Leon, "The median pay for full-time writers was $20,300 in 2017, and that number decreased to $6,080 when part-time writers were considered." As of this printing, the poverty line in the United States is about $3,000 *above* that.

This is why there are significantly more part-time writers than full-time writers. (It becomes obvious why we needed a #5AMWritersClub.)

The truth is, if you're going to enter this career, learning how published authors earn money will:
★ Help you decide if you even want to put in all that time and effort to write that book in the first place.
★ Show you why you must manage the marketing, so you can understand revenue streams.
★ Guide you to produce a smarter brand to better support the books you do write.

Advances and Royalties

Unless you're setting up a crowd-sourcing campaign, only traditionally published authors receive an advance—money for a book ahead of publishing.

For traditionally published authors, the publisher takes on the cost of book packaging (design, cover, editing, etc.) and handles some form of distribution. Once the book is published, the authors pay back the advance they received via royalties. Royalties are a percentage of book sales. They are earned one book at a time. Only once that advance is paid will authors receive any royalty checks. It can take months or years to begin receiving royalties, depending on the size of the advance. Why? Because royalties are smaller than you think.

Publishers typically grant 8-12% of sales on print books. 10-25% on audio books. And about 25% on ebooks. (If you have an agent, the agent takes 15% of royalties *before* you get paid. So you would receive, for example, 85% of that 8-12% on a print book.)

Indie authors do not get advances, and they s*pend money* in advance of publishing by managing the book packaging and distribution.

However, from day one of publication, indie authors receive royalties on every book sold, and almost always with a higher percentage of royalties compared to traditional authors. Amazon/KDP, for instance, provides ebook royalty options as either 35% or 70% depending on the price of your book. (See the **Author Earnings Chart.**)

For both types of authors (traditional or indie) royalties vary depending on where you sell your books—bookstores, online, or in person.

Three ways authors earn royalties for print books:

1. Physical bookstores
2. Online
3. Direct to readers

Whether you're an indie- or traditionally published author, on each printed copy of your book, you're earning royalties after the costs of printing and distribution are deducted. For example, on a $17.99, 400-page book, the costs to print and ship are about $8. With $8 deducted, an author's net royalties from that book are based on sales locations. For *print* copies, the breakdown is in the chart below.

It is true that online "bookshop" portals such as Bookshop.org pay additional royalties to authors. Although they still have to cover printing and shipping costs, the net is superior to online retailers or bookshops. (An example of my online store is here: https://karenachase.square.site/)

Ebooks take the least amount of time to produce. Because there are no printing and shipping costs, royalties can be higher per sale than print books.

Some genres (e.g., sci-fi, fantasy, romance) sell exceptionally well as ebooks or audio books, so print concerns might not be relevant to you, depending on your genre. (We'll get into this a bit in the section on target audience; however, how and which formats to produce is a topic for another book. For now let's get back to...)

Why Direct Sales Matters Most

Regardless of how you publish, you can see from the **Author Earnings Chart** that authors net the most by selling print books directly to readers at their presentations or events.

What's crystal clear from that chart is when you arrange a speaking gig, a table at a conference, or a talk at a book club, readers can buy the book directly from you, and that's when you earn the most per book.

Those direct sales have one even more impressive, long-term benefit. They allow authors to secure what neither Amazon nor a bookseller can—a memorable and lasting connection between you and your targeted readers. That moment strengthens the experience for the reader, making them more likely to purchase your next book.

Author Earnings Chart (Approximately, Per Print Book*)

SALES LOCATION	Retail Price	- Printing	- Retailer Discount	Net: Indie	Net: Traditional **
Bookstores (Indie/Chain/Giftshops)	$17.99	- $8.00	55% off retail (Bookstores pay just $9.89.)	$1.89	$1.61
Online (Amazon, B&N, iBooks, etc.)	$17.99	- $8.00	30% of each sale (They take $5.39 per book.)	$4.59	$3.90
Direct to Readers (Author Talks & Events)	$17.99	- $8.00	0	$9.99	$9.89

* Prices of printing fluctuate with paper. Bookstore discounts and online retailer percentages are also subject to change.
** The traditional author typically receives a few courtesy copies at the time of publishing. But to hand-sell books directly, traditional authors typically purchase their own book at cost or wholesale costs (55% discount) from their publisher. At $17.99, the wholesale cost is $9.89. The net for traditional with bookstores and chains shown is after the 15% agent fee is deducted.

Direct sales allow you to provide more of an experience (your service) AND you earn enough money to keep doing more of what you love. That combination is priceless.

Now that you know the approximate financial realities, regardless of whether you're indie- or traditionally published, you must learn to spend your time and money wisely to connect directly with those readers.

This is why you need to create a plan that defines exactly who those readers are and will be and where they hang out. This is why Willy & Nilly can't be a part of any author platform plan.

If you're ready to make a plan to be the best *Author Entrepreneur* you can be, then as a bonus let's dispel one final outdated belief.

Bonus Outdated Belief:
Authors need to stay in one lane.

Some in the traditional world believe that if you write romance, heaven forbid you should suddenly write cozy mysteries.

Publishers encourage authors to stay in one genre because a publisher's marketing is tied to promoting products by the truckload. Thus, it's difficult to promote engine oil when you've built an audience of olive oil enthusiasts.

And yet, many authors are capable of writing across genres and love the challenge. Stephen King published, among others, the *Shawshank Redemption* (uplifting fiction), *Joyland* (noir crime), and of course *Carrie* (horror). Jaqueline Woodson, wrote for nearly every age of reader. *The Day you Begin* is a picture book, and she also wrote for middle-grade, young adult, and adult.

WHERE AUTHORS EARN:
(Approximation based on 100 print books)

SOLD VIA BOOKSTORE = $200

SOLD ON AMAZON = $400

SOLD DIRECTLY TO READERS = $750 – $900
PLUS YOUR READERS ARE
MORE LIKELY BUY OTHER BOOKS

Tidbit WE NEED TO LEARN ABOUT PUBLISHING

Would a lawyer never learn about the judicial system? Would an accountant only add and subtract but not understand the ever-changing tax codes? No.

The more we authors understand the publishing industry—yes, branding and building platform tools, but also how books are made and distributed—you will gain at least two advantages. You'll work more efficiently within reality. And it's less likely you'll be taken advantage of by those overcharging or underserving authors .

To gain and share knowledge, you can join the Author's Guild (AuthorsGuild.org), or communicate your concerns at writing conferences and with agents, booksellers, or publishers you know. (Or better yet, buy them all a copy of this workbook!)

The current publishing climate is forcing authors to manage so many marketing and brand tasks, so your best two options if you want to continue to write and publish is to develop tools in order to:
  ★ Grow your readership while pursuing traditional publishing *while you also*
  ★ Learn all you can about publishing books independently.

P.S.: All authors will be publishing independently if traditional publishers buckle and fold—just like the major record labels did due to the emergence of iTunes. Between publishing houses merging, layoffs in the face of the Covid-19 pandemic, major authors indie-publishing, more agents available than publishers, and the "Great Resignation" of editors who are overworked and underpaid (yet, still paid more than most authors)—well, the end of traditional publishing might be a-comin', and you need a bunker.

True, many authors are already super famous when they switched, but let's study this one-lane notion from a reader's perspective.

How many readers do you know read only one genre and never, ever pick up anything else? Very few, if any, right?

In this publishing climate of shrinking dollars, authors need to publish more books and broaden their reader base to make a living. Adding genres expands their offerings. Even I, an indie-published author of fiction, have expanded my offerings by publishing this practical nonfiction workbook. I'm also producing short stories.

I made these shifts to expand my options and invite more readers. You can, too. Plus, crossing genres can be fun and extremely liberating. Each new genre means more writing and more readers, which leads to more writing.

But how do you create a plan that grows with a widening writing career? I give you the title of this book: **Brand the Author (Not the Book)**.

Brand The Author

I have yet to meet an author who dreams of being a one-hit wonder.

You probably envision multiple books as a way to retire from ____ (insert your current profession here). If you want to write full time, you need more than one book, which means you need to develop platform tools to capture readers early. Then the majority of them will come along with you for each subsequent book.

Plus, remember our wine analogy? Creating websites and social media profiles for each book is akin to a vintner building tasting rooms for each wine—one for Chardonnay, one for Pinot Gris, another for the Pinot Noir—which is ludicrous.

Separate brands divide your audience and doing that is financially unsustainable. You want everyone drinking in one room and sampling everything, so you need to build platform tools geared toward their engagement with you, the author.

True, you can buy the URL for each of your books and then point that website URL back to your main website. But you first need a brand plan; your URL discussions come after figuring out which platform tools are best for you.

Platform what? Yes, all these terms—platform, tools, brand—can be confusing. So before we dive into building your plan, let's look at basic definitions about the pieces you'll be building in this workbook and why you'll need them.

Tidbit BRAND LOYALTY = AUTHOR LOYALTY

In a September 23, 2020, online blog post published by Jane Friedman entitled "Amazon's Importance to US Book Sales Keeps Increasing—for Better or Worse," Peter Hildick-Smith of the research firm Codex Group said it best:

"The hallmark of successful fiction publishing is sustaining loyalty to a brand, and the number-one factor in a decision to buy a new book is whether the author is someone the reader knows and likes."

Readers pick up books because of their authors.
It's your job to keep those readers loyal.

If you're not following Jane Friedman, you ought to. She has the best industry knowledge because she is an industry insider. Formerly an editor for publishers, she is now an author consultant who offers online classes. You can sign up for her newsletter and her *Hot Sheet* at janefriedman.com. Now. Off you go... I will wait right here until you've subscribed.

TERMS FOR THIS WORKBOOK

Certain words and phrases are bandied about all the time in publishing, but they don't always make sense. You may have attended enough writing conferences to recognize that even people in marketing and publishing aren't consistently using the terms noted here. In an effort to clear things up and get everyone on the same page for this workbook, let's address the book marketing terms.

Author Platform

When authors (either before their books come out or after they're published) grow a loyal following of readers, how/where they hear about an author's book is called the author platform. It's a combination of four factors—all seen in the TV show *Gilmore Girls*:

★ *Message*—an announcement shouted to the citizens of Stars Hollow from the gazebo
★ *Target Audience*—the Stars Hollow citizens gathered to hear it
★ *Platform Tools*—the gazebo and the directional signs to it
★ *Brand Elements*—the gazebo they see and experience

If your message and tools are built effectively, those in your target audience will be so invested in your platform, they will personally deliver that message to anyone drinking coffee with Lorelai and Rory at Luke's Diner.

If you need to run off and watch a few episodes to understand my analogy, I'll wait here. For those who have already seen the show, let's start with the author message...

Terms you'll need to know...

Author Message
(the announcement from the gazebo)

I know you have something to say. You wrote a book! But your author message is not the subject of that book. Rather, your author message is tied to why you wrote that book.

For instance, my first novel, *Carrying Independence*, is about a guy hired to help gather the final signatures on the Declaration of Independence. But *why* I wrote this story has nothing to do with the document. I firmly believe we can learn about ourselves by traveling and engaging in history.

Sure, other authors are also motivated by one or both of those things, but when I couple my belief with my particular brand of humor and unbridled nerdy enthusiasm, my author message becomes intrinsically mine. It becomes my purpose, and one my readers can experience with me. They can #TravelWithAdventure while #ChasingHistories, too.

For some authors, the reason they write is to provide an escape. For others, it may be to debunk faulty thinking. Once you define your message, which you'll do in **Section 2: Author Message**, you must figure out how to share your message.

Yes, regardless of your book(s) or topics(s), you need to know who your readers are.

Target Audience
(the citizens gathering
around the gazebo)

These are the loyal readers most likely to gather around your gazebo (real or virtual) that eagerly want to connect with you. If you are a Young Adult (YA) author, yet your Twitter feed and primary contacts are moms and librarians, you're speaking to the wrong crowd. Or, as I said to a YA author with this problem, your target audience of teenagers is talking about books in the cafeteria while you're hanging out in the teachers' lounge sounding like a boring grown-up.

Yes, librarians will recommend books, but authors need to connect with the bullseye of their target— the people *most likely* to jam their noses into your book and who will then turn to their friend and say, "You also have to jam your nose into this book."

Your readers have a definable list of demographics that includes age, gender, and ethnicity. They also hang out in certain places—online and physically. They have other books, magazines, movies, vocabulary, and activities they love (or hate). For example, if you write Georgian romances, your readers are likely women ages 16 to 65 who read Jane Austen, follow Colin Firth, know the difference between corsets and stays, and might be members of Regency Societies.

You'll get a chance to define these characteristics in **Section 3: Primary Target Audience**, so you know where you need to interact with your readers. Your audience will also need to interact with you, which is why you need platform tools.

Platform Tools
(the gazebo and directional signs to it)

If all you have is a gazebo from which to sell your book, your readers will consist of only those citizens who happen to come to the town square. That means you need to think bigger, broader.

A platform tool is anything a reader will engage with that comes from you. If they can see it, touch it, or hear it, it's a platform tool. If you're a cookbook author or your novel includes recipes in the back, your loyal readers may even taste it!

Tools, like directional signage pointing to the gazebo, are the means by which your target audience finds and engages with you. What are your primary tools? Your book(s), website, and newsletter. You also have social media, advertising, publicity, presentations, and even printed materials such as bookmarks and business cards.

However, not all platform tools are effective at capturing your particular target audience. YA readers are less likely to be on Facebook than on Instagram, for example. And AARP events and retirement communities won't be ideal places for middle-grade authors to give presentations.

Fret not. In **Section 4: Primary Platform Tools**, this workbook will help you narrow down which tools are best for you and prioritize which ones to build first.

Author Brand Elements
(the gazebo they see and experience)

Going back to our *Gilmore Girls* reference, when the citizens of Stars Hollow gather around to hear your message at that gazebo, what pray-tell does your gazebo look like? Does it look like a faded Victorian postcard, the colorful Barkcloth of Uganda, or a sleek Asten Martin a là James Bond?

Brand elements consist of the author photo, the colors on your materials, the fonts that grace all your printed materials, and the way all those elements work together.

Brand elements are NOT designed using the cover of your books. *Let me repeat.* Your brand elements are *not* to be designed to match the covers of your books.

Each book design has its own set of brand elements. Those are not yours. Why? Because book covers can vary wildly. You might not always have the same publisher or designer. You might write across genres, so you don't want sci-fi to look like romance. Three of your books could be repackaged and their covers redesigned.

Because book design does not affect your long-term author image, this requires choosing brand elements through a process of careful consideration based on your message, audience, and platform tools. **Section 5: Brand Elements** will guide you through choosing your image wisely so it will last. You must also restrain yourself and keep these elements simple. Too many fonts or colors can lead to inconsistencies. Having fewer elements can contribute to greater longevity.

All these brand elements, platform tools, and messaging come together to be your...

Author Brand

An author brand is the experience (the feeling) your readers have when they hear your message and interact with your particular platform tools.

Think of the brands you are most loyal to. What do you see? How do you feel about them? If I say Coca-Cola®, you can see the swirling font, the red color, the shape of the bottle. You might also get nostalgic about those warm and fuzzy holiday commercials with the polar bears. All of that adds up to how you *feel* about the brand. The same applies to authors. Remember what a brand is?

An author brand is your <u>unique</u> collection of fonts, colors, words, and imagery that are <u>consistently</u> applied to your platform tools to <u>authentically</u> convey your message to your readers.

Every effective brand has those three underlined characteristics going for it:

Unique. Consistent. Authentic.

First, that feeling you have about a brand must be unique. REI® branding is different from Patagonia® even though they both sell outdoor gear.

Look at branding for Sadeqa Johnson versus Danielle Steel. Readers feel something different for each of these authors even though they both write historical fiction. Authors, like brands, can't copy one another.

*Brand plagiarism breeds apathy.
Uniqueness breeds loyalty.
Be who you are.
Own who you are.*

Second, a brand is crafted through consistency. If an author's PowerPoint presentation looks like his or her website, which also looks like the author's Twitter page, then readers can be certain of who they're following. Coca-Cola® has had that same logo since 1886—it's consistent, even if the company's ad campaigns change every year.

The opposite is also true. If the business card an author hands you is gorgeous but the website reads "under construction," the inconsistency is glaring. Too many different fonts? Inconsistent. No online presence except on Amazon? Inconsistent.

*Inconsistency breeds confusion.
Consistency breeds loyalty.*

Third, your brand has to be authentic. We live in a transparent world and audiences are getting better at pointing out B.S. when they see it. B.S. = Brand Stupidity.

B.S. happens when a brand says one thing but the reality and/or actions are quite another. (Most politicians come to mind.) The way to counter B.S. or inauthenticity is with its opposite: Authenticity.

That's especially important when it comes to your author message. For example, I love nearly everything about traveling, and I believe travel is necessary to understanding history. However, if I secretly hated traveling and never left home, eventually my inauthenticity would catch up with me. Your words and actions have to match.

*Inauthenticity breeds abandonment.
Authenticity breeds loyalty.*

Loyalty breeds sustainabilty.

NO B.S.
ONLY YOU CAN BE…

———

UNIQUE.
CONSISTENT.
AUTHENTIC.

———

A Word On Hybrid Publishing

A multitude of hybrid publishers are out there, and their overall business model is simple: authors pay a fee to publish through them. How much? $5000? $10,000? Yes, even upwards of $50,000! PLEASE read the **Tidtbit** here, and if you're still entertaining this avenue, be sure to ask the following questions:

What do I get for online distribution?

Most hybrids promise to publish (upload) to online retailers in the form of an ebook. Some also promise to fulfill print orders via those same online retailers using print-on-demand (POD). POD means books are printed only when they're ordered; there is no pre-printed supply in a warehouse. Uploading files and using POD companies (there are several options although some may not include distribution to retailers) is exactly what you would be doing as an indie-published author. If the hybrid is offering more in terms of keyword and algorithm marketing, only then is their online distribution more robust than yours.

What do I get for bookstore and library distribution?

Many hybrid publishers describe their distribution as "we make your book available" via Ingram (the company from which most bookstores order books). "Available" does not mean the hybrid publisher sends sales reps store to store pitching new book titles like the major publishers do. It means bookstores and libraries will only know about your book when someone tells them it is listed on Ingram.

If your hybrid publisher isn't pitching the book to retailers, then that task falls to you. You don't mind, you say? Membership in the American Booksellers Association rose to 1,910 in 2021 according to Allison Hill, CEO.* That number doesn't include Barnes & Noble, airport bookstores like Hudson, or other chain retail outlets. Are you seriously going to contact more than 2,000 retailers yourself? Making something "available" is NOT distribution. Period.

What is the book marketing plan?

Okay, so if the hybrid publisher won't distribute your book to bookstores, will it at least manage some of the marketing? Some of these hybrids provide marketing, which ranges from thirty days to three months of marketing effort to ongoing consultations. Some offer none at all. If the hybrids you approach offer marketing, ask them to break down what they mean by "marketing."

What is the plan? How long will it last? Is it online only? Is it social media? Is it Amazon ads? Is it reviews that are paid for, and if so, who is paying for them? Will they send press releases to major magazines, run a blog tour, or will there be ads or award submissions, too? And if any sort of marketing plan exists, in addition to asking who pays for what, I also suggest you immediately ask this next question...

*Another Pandemic Surprise: A Mini Indie Bookstore Boom by Judith Rosen, Publishers Weekly, October 15, 2021

ASK NOT
WHAT HYBRIDS WILL
DO FOR YOU, BUT WHAT TOGETHER
WE CAN DO FOR ALL AUTHORS.

What is the ROI?

ROI is the return on investment. What will yours be? Let's say you spend $20,000 with a hybrid publisher (for book packaging, uploading, marketing, etc.). At $17.99, your would need to sell more than 2200 copies directly to readers ($8 profit/copy) just to pay off the $20,000. That's *before* you earn money!

If you sold print books online only ($2 profit/copy) you'd have to move 10,000 books. (Remember, most books don't sell 5000 copies in a lifetime.)

Very few hybrids have ROI data or statistics. I know; I've asked. You should ask, too. We all should. And if they don't have data, or won't share it, then question *everything* about their business model.

Here's an example of why questioning them is so important. During my research when I asked this of a hybrid publisher (who wanted to publish my book) they admitted to me, "We don't have numbers, but we do know hardly any of our authors make back the money they spend with us." *Wow. Holy crap.*

𝒯𝑖𝑑𝑏𝑖𝑡 ARE WE KILLING OUR OWN PROFESSION?

Would a bookseller pay customers to take home books with no expectation about when the customer would purchase one? Would lawyers work in a firm without promise of a commission or salary? Would a plumber pay *you* to fix your toilet? *No. No. No*!

To make authorship a true profession—one in which writers can work full time—we must be paid *equitably* for our craft. Period. Yet, by agreeing to pay-to-play, too many authors and publishers are turning writing into a hobby—an *expensive* one*. So ALL authors must ask:

★ What is the value of an author?
★ What is my value as an author?

If *any* publisher (hybrid or traditional) asks authors to pay upfront <u>and</u> cannot faithfully help you earn out your investment, then you are agreeing your creative talents, and our profession, have no monetary value.

We must be Author Entrepreneurs and hire vendors to help us publish our books with costs that still allow us to earn beyond the investment.

* Consider this: A kit to make your own MK4 roadster begins at $12,000. When you're done, you'd know how to build an engine and have a friggin' car to show for that hobby. And you wouldn't have to do any marketing in order to have people see it. Just drive around. Care free.

Write. It. Down.

You wouldn't publish a book
with blank pages,
so why would you create a brand
without a written plan?

PART II

*THE WRITTEN BRAND
PLAN WORKBOOK*

———

I AM THE BOSS OF ME.

———

EXCEPT WHEN I'M NOT.

Welcome to the main workbook.

PART II consists of six sections. Be sure to work on them in order and complete each section before moving on to the next.

Section One

Get Yourself Organized
Preparing for the work ahead by evaluating and establishing structures for:
★ Documents
★ Time
★ Tasks

Section Two

Author Message
Defining—in a single paragraph—who you are, why you write, and the benefit your writing provides for your readers.

Section Three

Target Audience
Examining and establishing your primary reader and fellow-author profiles.

Section Four

Platform Tools
Learning about the marketing funnel and establishing which platform tools are best suited to share your message with your audience.

Section Five

Brand Elements
Choosing the visuals that will best convey you and your message to your audience based upon the work in previous sections and your own style.

Section Six

Final Brand Plan
Gathering all your decisions from previous sections into a master document that is coupled with a platform tools priority checklist.

SECTION 1
GET YOURSELF ORGANIZED

No plan will come to fruition if you haven't properly determined how to navigate toward your author goals. You need filing systems you can stick with. You need an *honest* assessment of your life commitments so you can allocate time to your goals. And you definitely need to know which of the tasks required to build this brand are best suited to your skills and attitude.

If it sounds to you like this section is about planning to plan, it is. Here, you'll make decisions about how to organize your:

DOCUMENTS. TIME. TASKS.

Document Maintenance

Although this is a workbook and the print version provides spaces to write in answers about your brand plans, you still need a long-term place to house your notes, ideas, and decisions. That's true, even if you've purchased the ebook version of this workbook.

When you've finished all the sections you'll have a document known as your **Final Brand Plan**. Where will you keep all the pieces associated with your plan—both physically and digitally?

STEP 1:
PICK A PHYSICAL STORAGE
OPTION FOR NOTES AND PAPERS.

This should not be a journal you also use for creative writing or the binder containing your child's soccer schedule. You need a dedicated (gasp, fresh) spot only for your *Author Brand Plan* documents.

If it helps to run to the office supply store or consult with Martha Stewart about the perfect filing system, do it. This is supposed to be fun. (And who doesn't love the smell of potential within fresh office supplies?) Remember, though, you're not curing cancer here, so be decisive while keeping it simple. You can choose from:

★ A notebook with a pocket or two
★ A binder with interior pockets
★ A Trapper Keeper® binder with pockets*
★ An accordion file
★ A file box with colorful file folders

*My personal favorite—I was a teenager in the '80s.

STEP 2:
ESTABLISH A COMPUTER FILING SYSTEM

While using the ebook version, or perhaps even while using this print version, you'll need consistent file folders for storing your notes, too. Head to your computer and create folders with these titles:

★ MY AUTHOR BRAND (MAIN)
★ Brand Plan (Subfolder)
★ Platform Tools Plan (Subfolder)
★ Working Notes (Subfolder)
★ Brand Element Ideas (Subfolder)

STEP 3:
COMMIT TO YOUR SELECTIONS

❑ I have chosen to a physical document organization method for my brand plan and notes.
❑ I have set up my digital document folders.

Schedules & Time Management

In this section, you'll decide when you'll work on the business aspects (including this workbook) associated with your *Author Entrepreneur* life. But first, here's a little education.

Writers love to write; we'd rather be writing than doing just about anything else. Today's *Author Entrepreneurs* split their time in many ways, most of which can be divided into these three time-commitment categories.

★ Writing
★ Business
★ Life

That third one is a doozy—it is our paying jobs, our families, cleaning, laundry, cooking and exercise, social activities, holidays, etc. However, this is a workbook for authors, so let's focus on allocating time for the first two. Writing and business.

TIME DEDICATED TO BUSINESS VERSUS WRITING

How you spend your time as an *Author Entrepreneur*—business tasks versus writing—depends on where you are in the book development cycle, shown in the following chart.

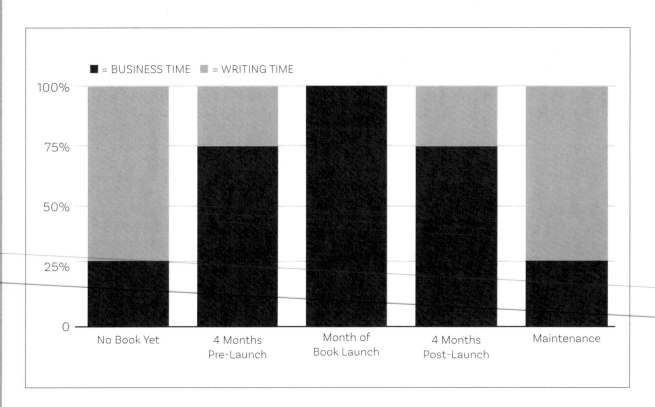

What do you instantly notice? That's right...

At no time are you only writing.

(Sorry.) Why? As stated earlier, authors' livelihoods are tied to the feeling they ignite in their readers. Remember the analogy of comparing an author to a vintner?

You need to spend time letting your readers know your book exists.

It's on you. You. You. Publishers will only do so much, because they typically publicize a book for about three to six months. That time can and must be expanded by you.* And if you are publishing independently, then it's all on you, honey, and those business tasks include marketing and publishing. Let's calculate how much time you'll need to do it well.

* What if your publisher wants you to begin on the next book immediately, and you have a short (aka ridiculous) deadline? Silence from you is still not an option. You need to budget dollars to hire professional help, like an author assistant, or perhaps an intern. (Please pay your interns. It results in increased reliability and it's just nice.) And you absolutely should ask for marketing dollars as part of any traditional publishing contract. You're going to need it.

Birthing the Book

You've probably heard writers use the phrase "birthing a book." The months associated with birth are also a smart way to look at the marketing time spent to launch a book. You need a sufficient gestational period to grow and strengthen your book and your connection with your readers when it is most valuable—that is, just before and after your book is published.

Consequently, during the *nine months* surrounding your book launch, your writing life must take a back seat to nurturing that birth. *

The nine-month book launch break-down:

Four months pre-launch: 75% marketing
Hype + anticipation = greater engagement/sales. These four months are for managing advance reader copies, pre-sales promotions, organizing and publicizing the launch event, sharing behind-the-scenes book tidbits, pitching articles, and conducting giveaways and promotions.

Launch month: 100% marketing
Your time is ALL about the business of launching that book. Or as I call it, shameless self-promotion. Not one single moment of this month is given to writing anything new unless it's a blog or article supporting the launch of the book.

Four months post-launch: 75% marketing
These final four months are about sharing pics of the launch, setting up reviews, managing publicity and podcasts, scheduling and making appearances, writing articles, blogging, establishing long-term book promotions, etc.

Dedicating this time will enable you to hear what one reader told me at my book launch. "I opened Instagram, and there you were. I passed the bookstore, you were in the window. I got a newsletter, and you were in it. I see your book *everywhere*. I had to come." Attendees shared their photos with their audiences online because I spent the time organizing an event worth posting about even though I'm kind of a self-published nobody.

True, people can get fatigued from seeing you *too* much. So, about four months after your launch-month, it's time to give readers a break from publicity and get your butt back into the chair to write. Again, you won't write 100% of the time, but now you can comfortably spend 75% of your author hours actually writing, with the remaining 25% of your hours dedicated to brand and business maintenance and advancement.

Okay, so how do you figure out how many hours that will actually be? Practically speaking, you need a *plan* (there's that word again). You do not want to guess at how many hours the 75%/25% split gives you; you want to *know*. Plus, you need to balance those hours with your third commitment—the reality of actual life. So, let's examine the actual life hours you have now.

---

* I often joked that if birthing a book was like birthing a baby, then my first novel—from idea to publication—was equivalent to four wooly mammoths (ten years). It was exhausting.

Life Hours

It is time for an honest examination of the available hours in your life. Not all of them—just those that are immoveable. Take a stab at it yourself, but I also recommend you consult with people in your household about their expectations and aspirations, too.

If you're pursuing writing as a second career or as a career change, having your household members on board is not only thoughtful, it makes the journey infinitely easier. And if you have children, it teaches them that writing is a legitimate career path fueled by a passion to share meaningful messages.

So, what's expected of you, and what are your expectations? Fill in the hours that exist now.

TASK	HOURS
A Full-time or Part-time job	
Family or Friend Time	
Household Chores	
Other Commitments (E.g. cooking, groceries, repairs, etc.)	
Reading or Watching TV (Aka other people's writing)	
Other Hours:	
TOTAL HOURS for life	
Subtract the above TOTAL from 112 = TOTAL HOURS Writing & Business	

Why 112? There are 168 hours in a week. Eight hours is recommended for bedtime/sleep, which leaves 112 waking hours. What if your hours *for life* are greater than 112? To pursue a writing career, you'll have to adjust (I got rid of my TV). For some, it may be this just isn't the right time given your commitments—find small moments to write for the joy of it instead.

Author Hours

Given what you now know about your life commitments, when do you normally write? (Because you have the time, can make the time, or you are at your best creatively.)

This doesn't include those moments when you jot down a grand idea at 3 a.m. after your head pops off the pillow. Rather, author hours are the reasonable, regular "office hours" you can and will dedicate to your *Author Entrepreneur* business life.

Remember, these are the business hours of your *Author Entrepreneur* life. There's no writing at this time, so you might want to ensure that scheduled business time is treated differently. Put on a "Boss" hat, wear a suit, or work in a different room during the business hours if it makes you more productive or gets you into that head space.

Managing your own business does, however, comes with a fun perk. Holidays.

About six months after I left a full-time job and began freelancing in branding and design (in 2004), it magically occurred to me that I didn't have to ask for permission to take time off. So, I took two weeks off in July, another week for my birthday, and another two weeks at the end of the year. After a year in business, I took off Friday afternoons.

Even part-time authors need breaks, too. Then we can engage with life, which helps us write about it better. Knowing a break is ahead—from both the writing and business tasks—will help you work more efficiently because your *Author Entrepreneur* life won't seem quite so endless.

It's your own business—and you're the boss of it—so let's define your business days/hours and holidays.

My Author Entrepreneur Hours & Holidays will be:

I will work as an Author Entrepreneur
these days of the week (check all that apply):

      S   M   T   W   T   F   S

Time of Day (check all that apply):

    AM   PM

For each of the above, how many writing hours per session and when?
(E.g., If you can make only Sunday morning 8 a.m. until noon, that's 4 hours.)

TOTAL AUTHOR HOURS PER WEEK: _____

Now, look back at that writing/business hours division chart. Divide your total weekly hours by the percentage, and insert the hours below. For example, if you have just four hours a week, you'll dedicate three hours to writing and one hour to business if you don't have a book yet.

Those business hours will become the times you work on this workbook and brand plan going forward. It's up to you to decide when to schedule the business hours each week.

My Author Entrepreneur hours:

No Book Yet: Writing Hours (75%) _____ Business Hours (25%) _____ per week

Pre- & Post-Launch: Writing Hours (25%) _____ Business Hours (75%) _____ per week

Launch Month: Writing Hours (0%) _____ Business Hours (100%) _____ per week

Annually, I will take Author Entrepreneur vacations:
(number of weeks) and at minimum during these dates (list all)

Tasks and Competencies

The last step in **Section 1** is to establish which of the brand development tasks you're *capable* of doing on your own, and which you *prefer* to do with others. In this section, you'll rate yourself in these areas based on SKILL and JOY.

As you insert your answers, keep in mind the "office hours" you've just committed to. If you have only four hours of *Author Entrepreneur* life per week, do you really want to spend them learning to code websites? Maybe you do. For me, coding my own website was as ridiculous as installing a printing press in my living room.* I suck at it, and I'd rather die than do it.

SKILL: On a scale of 1-10, how competent are you at doing the tasks in the chart?

1 = I suck   10 = I'm awesome

JOY: On a scale of 1-10, how much do you enjoy doing the following tasks in the chart?

1 = I'd rather die   10 = I'm totally up for it

*Incidentally, Virginia Woolf did install a printing press in her living room as she was forced to independently publish her own books. Two good points (among many) to learn here. Publishing has a history of not always being what authors need to produce their best work. Self-publishing has been around longer than you think.

TASK (Alphabetically)	SKILL	JOY
Advertising Development		
Copywriting		
Event Planning		
Illustration		
Newsletter Development		
Newsletter e-Mailings		
Photography		
Power Point Development		
Print Design		
Print Production (Printing)		
Publicity/Press Releases		
Scheduling Events		
Social Media Development		
Social Media Posts/Updates		
Web Design		
Web Programming		
Other:		

BEING A STRONG BOSS MEANS HAVING THE GRACE TO RECOGNIZE WHERE YOU ARE WEAK.

And if you suck at these tasks and you'd rather die than do any of them, you'll need to budget in more time and money to hire help (addressed in **Section 4: Platform Tools**). Or it may be time to examine what you expect from publishing given the reality of authorship today.

DO IT YOURSELF VERSUS HIRING HELP

Now, it's time to commit to which tasks you're going to do versus those you'll need help with. In the chart below, assign a letter to your tasks based on your rankings.

True, this outcome is tied to what you can afford to do on your own versus hiring a professional, like an author assistant, or an intern to help you. If you have little budget funds or none at all for help (and we'll talk about budgets in the **Primary Platform Tools** section), the task will take you longer to complete.

Dollars aren't important now; assigning roles based on your skills and joy is.

Put a letter next to each task. Some tasks may have both letters.
H = HELP from Professionals or Support Staff
O = OWNER (that's you)

TASK	H	O
Copywriting		
Photography		
Illustration		
Web Design		
Web Programming		
Print Design		
Print Production (Printing)		
Newsletter Development		
Newsletter e-Mailings		
Social Media Set-up		
Social Media Posts/updates		
Publicity		
Advertising		
Scheduling Events		
Event Planning		
Power Point Development		
Other:		

NOTES
I know you have thoughts to write down. Here's some space for ya:

SECTION 1: GET YOURSELF ORGANIZED
Summary of Decisions

By the time you reach this page, you've hopefully made firm decisions about various aspects of your *Author Entrepreneur* business. The sections here are set up with blanks and checkboxes, so your chest can swell with that warm feeling of accomplishment as you fill them in, and check, check, check.

Remember, even if you're using the print version of this workbook, you can instead create a digital document with the information below. If you do, label your file "Section 1 Decisions," and keep it in the computer folder titled "Working Notes."

DOCUMENT MAINTENANCE

My physical storage options for notes and documents is: _____

❑   I have set up folders on my computer.

My Author Entrepreneur office hours are:

_____ (days of the week)
_____ (hours per session)
Total: _____ (hours per week)

This makes my Author Entrepreneur hours:

No Book Yet:
Writing Hours (75%) _____ per week
Business Hours (25%) _____ per week

Pre- & Post-Launch:
Writing Hours (25%) _____ per week
Business Hours (75%) _____ per week

Launch Month:
Writing Hours (0%) _____ per week
Business Hours (100%) _____ per week

My Writing Hours will generally be at:
_____ (this day/time)
My Business Hours will generally be at:
_____ (this day/time)

My holidays/vacations will be: _____
_____
_____

Tasks and Competencies

❑   Evaluated my SKILL level
❑   Evaluated my JOY level
❑   Assigned tasks to owner (O) or to help (H) as noted below:

TASK	Assigned to
Advertising Development	
Copywriting	
Event Planning	
Illustration	
Newsletter Development	
Newsletter e-Mailings	
Photography	
Power Point Development	
Print Design	
Print Production (Printing)	
Publicity/Press Releases	
Scheduling Events	
Social Media Development	
Social Media Posts/Updates	
Web Design	
Web Programming	
Other:	

Note: If you have not yet checked all the boxes, do not plow ahead into **Section 2: Author Message**. Go back and complete your work, honey. (Don't make me use that "mom tone" this early in the workbook.)

TIME IS MONEY, HONEY.

YOU DON'T GET THE LATTER WITHOUT PUTTING IN THE FORMER.

SECTION 2
AUTHOR
MESSAGE

(the announcement from the gazebo)

You know the mission statements that corporations have? Roll your eyes all you want, but when a mission statement is authentic and consistently applied, it aligns its employees with a common cause.

Similarly, think of the author message as your mission statement to help readers rally around you and bring others to your gazebo. You don't necessarily post this statement verbatim on your website, but you do share it via your text, colors, tone of voice, and general feel of your brand.

However, you must define your purpose for yourself before you can share it. In this section, you'll determine:

*WHO YOU ARE, WHY YOU WRITE WHAT YOU DO, & WHAT BENEFIT YOU BRING TO YOUR READERS**

*and why they will come to adore you!

Author Message

Earlier we went over how an effective brand has three characteristics going for it:

Unique. Consistent. Authentic.

To personify all three of these elements, you need to determine, specifically, what makes you… well, you.

What do you bring to this whole writing experience that no one else does—and why?

I'm not talking about your resumé, which is valid, especially if you write nonfiction. But a resumé tends to be an impersonal list of accomplishments. Here, we're exploring aspects of your writing life that are *highly* personal.

This is when you have to be honest. *Super-duper honest.* Deeply and truly on-your-knees honest. So honest even Yoda would say, "A Jedi master of your own force, you are."

Here are three situations requiring truth-telling:
★ If you write erotica but tell your mother it's romance—for her it's still romance, but in this workbook, it's erotica.
★ If you say you're an organizing guru, but you don't know who Marie Kondo is—uhm, no.
★ If you write about being easy going, but you've signed up for an anger management class—well, welcome to the dark side.

If you are from the dark side, it's okay—even controversial or anger-filled authors have amazing empires of followers (and according to my friend, Katharine, the dark side has cookies). Just don't fake your darkness. Be real. If you are authentically dark or grumpy, own it. And for you, Twitter may be an ideal platform tool.

STEP 1:
THE WORD SALAD

To define that special force within you, start by selecting words. Using the space provided here (in the print version, or the paper in the Trapper Keeper® you might be using) write down three or four *words* that define each of the following:

★ My best experiences (work, hobbies, life) before writing
★ My writing expertise, style, or approach
★ My preferred genre(s), topics(s)
★ Paid writing-related gigs beyond books I'd love to do (e.g., ghost-writing, articles, stand-up comedy, etc.)
★ My preferred and specific era or time-period
★ An ideology or approach to life I authentically live by
★ The way I describe my personality
★ The way my closest family and friends describe my personality. (If you're baffled, ask them directly; you might learn something!)

THE WORD SALAD

_____   _____   _____

_____   _____   _____

_____   _____   _____

_____   _____   _____

_____   _____   _____

_____   _____   _____

_____   _____   _____

STEP 2 :
AUTHOR STATEMENTS

Using the appropriate words from **The Word Salad**, build the following three statements. Write each statement as a concise sentence no longer than a tweet.

Your One Story Theme

Rosemary Rawlins, author of _All My Silent Years_, says authors have a central theme running through all their stories. For instance, whether my stories are fiction or nonfiction travel essays, they are about traveling from home so I can discover joy and independence. What's your one single story theme?

Your Bio Line

A bio line describes the factors that make you uniquely you based on your experience, personality, and/or approach. For instance, the crime novelist Bradley Harper, author of *A Knife in the Fog*, sees the world through an introspective yet joyful lens developed from his experiences as a career army pathologist and his seasonal job as Santa.

Brad's bio line is that actual sentence. He is the only crime novelist who fits that description: I suspect there is no one like you in your genre, and your uniqueness would show up in your bio line.

Do you empathize with the elderly because you care for an aging parent? Does your work as an actuary make you particularly adept at writing about risk? Using specific words from **The Word Salad** list, write down what you deeply believe makes you the writer you are.

Your Message to Readers

What do you hope readers glean from your work?

If you've been writing without thinking about your readers—which isn't unusual—do so now. What lesson or takeaway do you hope they get from you through your book(s)?

Your message doesn't have to be world changing. For example, romance novelist Mary Chris Escobar, author of *Delayed*, once told me she hopes her writing gives people a light escape while on holiday or whenever they need it most. That is an important contribution in itself.

Often, your message is tied to the words you listed for your approach to life. For instance, you might strive to live without fear. This surely seeps into your writing, so the word *fearless* might be in your message.

For fiction, you can include the genre(s) here. For nonfiction authors, your message might be related to your primary subjects, category, or the wisdom you hope to impart. So if you write about the afterlife or what we can learn from death and dying, include it here.

STEP THREE: EDITING

Link all three sentences together, joining them into one easily read paragraph. One paragraph! Once you have it down, work on it, sleep on it, and come back to it in the morning. Remember, editing is the hallmark of a great writer, so refine your author message.

SECTION 2: AUTHOR MESSAGE
Summary of Decisions

Writers have to stop editing at some point or they'll never publish.

When you're ready to commit to your author message, write that single paragraph of three sentences here one last time before turning to the next section. If you're keeping decisions on your computer, too, create a new document labeled, "Section2_Decisions" and store it in the subfolder you created called "Working Notes."

MY AUTHOR MESSAGE IS:

—————

EDITING ISN'T FOR SISSIES.

—————

NEITHER IS GETTING OLDER BUT BOTH MAKE US WISER.

SECTION 3
TARGET AUDIENCE

(the citizens gathering around the gazebo)

Readers come in all shapes and sizes, with various habits, likes and dislikes, moods and desires. They also have purchasing power and inhabit certain places—physically and online.

Thankfully, readers run in packs. Once you identify your pack, you can more easily choose the right gear needed to run with them. And once you're a trusted member, you'll more easily direct them back to your gazebo.

In this section, you'll create profiles for your:

PRIMARY READERS &*
FELLOW AUTHORS

*and perhaps secondary or tertiary readers.

Primary Target Audience

Adults who revel in the darkest Stephen King novels have a different set of behaviors and view-points than the hopeful young adults who pick up the Pakistan-based contemporary novels of Aisha Saeed. True, many people read widely, but your goal is to define the readers most likely to:

★ Read/hear what you have to say
★ Engage with you
★ Refer someone to you
★ Buy your book(s)
★ Buy your fellow authors' book(s)

It's not enough to guess or assume who those readers are. You need to study your audience—their actions and motivations—so you can apply fact-based knowledge to your brand. For this, let's use a tool you likely used in elementary school: the *5WH graphic organizer*.

When journalists or detectives set about creating the profile of a subject, they examine the basics—defining who, what, where, when, why (5W) and how (H)—in relation to a topic square placed at the center. You'll do the same.

Each topic has consistencies—even a few clichés—about what those readers enjoy and consume. Let's take British cozy mysteries for example.

Cozy mysteries is the *topic*. Those readers typically love tea (*what*), and they are more likely women (*who*), who might also hit antique shops (*where*).

You'll notice in the author's graphic organizer— **the 5WH+2 Graphic Organizer**— I've given you two additional spaces for *hobbies* and *purchases*.

Mystery readers might also knit (*hobbies*). Or they might also make donations to local gardening clubs (I count these as *purchases*)—you might later give presentations for your book at such garden clubs.

STEP ONE: MAKE A LIST OF TOPICS

Create a list of four or five topics about your book. For instance, Brad Harper's crime fiction I previously mentioned includes the topics of the Victorian era, London, forensics, and Sherlock Holmes. You might also include your genre here, but see the next **Tidbit** section for why genres are NOT helpful. List the best topics—for one book, or across all your books.

_____

_____

_____

_____

STEP TWO: USE GOOGLE TO EXPLORE THE TOPICS

Using one **5WH+2 Graphic Organizer** per topic (on separate sheets), you'll conduct online research. Focus on one topic at a time for about 90 minutes per topic. Begin by asking questions in Google related to your topic. Below are a few examples for one of Brad's topics—specifically Sherlock Holmes:

★ "Top Sherlock blogs, magazines, & websites"
★ "Top Sherlock conferences or events"
★ "Top Facebook (or Twitter or Instagram hashtags) groups related to Sherlock"
★ "Companies or organizations that Sherlock fans belong to"
★ "People who read Sherlock also buy…"
★ "Which authors do Sherlock fans follow?"

The 5WH+2 Graphic Organizer
Download this chart and others from the workbook via: **Bit.ly/KAC_BrandAuthor_BookFiles**

WHO	WHAT	WHERE

HOBBIES	*TOPIC*	WHEN

PURCHASES	HOW	WHY

Readers are people, and your primary people will be your best readers.

Within the Google results, read the most current information—look at the dates of posts and articles. As you get "spelunking" down through each Google result, you'll get more knowledgeable about your topic and learn terminology to help you better define specific search terms. Visit the social media sites you find.

Along the way, when you find another author, a social media influencer, a social media group, or a blog/newsletter that matches your topic, be sure to follow it or subscribe to it. Make a note in the WHO or WHERE section of your graphic organizer.

Remember, your ultimate goal with these **5WH+2 graphic organizers** is to learn about the *people* (aka readers and authors) who inhabit each topic's world. While so many things can go in the WHO bubble, it should absolutely include general demographics about your readers. List their average age, gender, ethnicity, geography/locations. If it's pertinent to your topic, you might also include professions or titles (e.g., moms, daughters, CEOs), or sexual or political orientations.

STEP THREE: CREATE THE PRIMARY TARGET AUDIENCE PROFILE

When you've tackled all your books' topics and the boxes are pretty full, spread the sheets on the floor and examine them collectively. Are there consistencies between the sheets in each of the **5WH+2** bubbles? If so, combine those topics and the top few results into one master **5WH+2** sheet. If not, pick the graphic organizer that is the most robust. Which one fits you and your work(s) the best?

That best-of-**5WH+2 Graphic Oranizer** sheet is now your *Primary Target Audience*. If there is a combination that is a close second, then it is your *Secondary Target Audience*.

Tidbit GENRES ARE NOT HELPFUL

After searching far and wide, I found what one writer called a *definitive* set of adult fiction genres:

★ Fantasy
★ Mystery
★ Romance
★ Science Fiction
★ Thriller and Suspense
★ Western
★ Horror

See anything missing? Historical fiction? Crime? Comedy? Women's fiction?

Those are considered sub-genres by some. And this is, in part, why agents reject books or worse, pitch the wrong editors. And yet, some things make it through, like the Sci-fi Western graphic novel *Cowboys and Aliens* by Scott Mitchell Rosenberg. Despite combining genres, it (and thousands of books by authors daring to mix it up) somehow found readers and was optioned for a film of the same name!

If you're confused by why agents and publishers would hamstring themselves with such maddeningly narrow and elusive descriptors, you're not alone. In a wonderful discussion between two authors whose books fit into multiple main genres, Neil Gaiman (*Coraline, American Gods,* and more) and Kazuo Ishiguro (*Remains of the Day, Never Let Me Go,* and others) gave their conclusions on genres that are the best I've heard yet.

Gaiman: "Genres only start existing when there's enough of them to form a sort of critical mass in a bookshop, and even that can go away."

Ishiguro: "I don't think they're helpful to anybody apart from publishers and bookshops."

Based on those comments, I hereby give you permission to learn about genres and then throw them out or use them only when and if it makes sense for you. As an *Author Entrepreneur,* your job is to know your specific target audience—not your book's genre—better than anyone else.

You can read the full discussion here: bit.ly/KAC_BrandAuthor4

Primary Fellow Author Profile

Before you say you're not like any other authors, uhm, yes, you are. If this sounds contrary to everything I've mentioned about the importance of being unique, hear me out.

As far as your brand message goes, your particular approach, life experience, and storytelling methods are uniquely *your* perspective.

From the reader's perspective, however, you won't be all that unique for long. Humans have an adaptive nature, a love of imposing order on chaos. We file huge amounts of data, jamming it into categories to simplify things, which then enables us to adapt more easily as we make selections. It's a long-ingrained habit.

When our ancestors walked by a bush with their friend, Bob, and a tiger popped out and ate Bob, the next time they saw that bush or even a similar one, they ran. That's one way they avoided being eaten.

Our categorizations can also let us expand our consumption. We know the differences between a book about a tiger that is "*The Life of Pi* meets Ursula Le Guin," and one that is "*The Life of Pi* meets Zane Grey." Because readers both *combine* and *expand* their preferences based upon what they've already read, you need to know...

Which authors are like you?

First, let's look at why I call them "fellow authors," and not comparative or competitive authors.

Authors are Not Comparative Nor Competitive

Agents and publishers particularly love these two classifications. We're encouraged to describe our work in query letters and nonfiction proposals by including "comparative" or "competitive" titles. When it comes to author brands and securing readers, these two descriptors don't quite suffice.

"Competitive" assumes all readers are narrow and insular in their reading habits. They assume readers will choose one book or author over another, but not choose both. And they assume readers can't be both loyal and exploratory. But they are!

"Comparative" suggests each author is less-than or greater-than another. While, it's true not all books or authors are created equal, this feels slightly combative, and suggests that I should view other Revolutionary-era indie-novelists such as Lars Hedbor and Libby Carter McNamee as authors to battle on the shelves.

But this isn't a war we're fighting. And if it is, what we seriously need is not a combative relationship but a band of brothers (and sisters). Consequently, in branding, I urge you to classify "other authors" using these two different words: *complementary* and *cooperative*.

Authors are Complementary and Cooperative

Complementary authors are those with books and brands somewhat different than ours, but we share a readership in some way. For example, many readers of *Outlander* also read Phillipa Gregory. In my world, David McCullough wrote *1776*, a nonfiction book about the first year of the Revolution. I don't know him; he's rather unreachable by little ol' me because of his illustrious publishing career. Yet, many of my same historical fiction readers loved his book, and many have told me so. Therefore, he is a *complementary* author.

Cooperative authors have books and brands that are similar to yours, just as Lars and Libby are to me. Furthermore, because I know them or can easily connect with them, we can grow our audiences through cooperation. We can tag within our social platforms, develop specific promotions, present together at conferences, recommend one another for speaking gigs, and more.

Your brand needs to reach your target audience, and that audience is already inhabiting the world of complementary and cooperative authors. So, who are they?

Just as you did with readers, next you'll craft a profile of your authors, including those who are:

Complementary:
Similar in some ways,
but you don't know them
or can't connect.

Cooperative:
Similar in more ways,
and you know them
or can easily connect.

STEP 1: MAKE TWO LISTS OF AUTHORS

Go back to your *Primary Target Audience* profile. Are there authors in the WHO or WHAT sections of your **5WH+2 graphic organizer**? If yes, write the names of those authors into the chart shown next. If no, you might need to revisit your *Primary Target Audience* profile and do some more research.

STEP 2: COMPLETE PRIMARY FELLOW AUTHOR PROFILE

For each of the authors in those categories, conduct an online search and define WHERE they hang out. Don't go hunting them down like a crazy stalker; instead, get to know them and start engaging authentically with them and their readers.

Because this author information is part of your written author brand plan that will inform your platform tool selection in **Section 4**, the chart also has spaces for you to list each author's:

★ Social Media Accounts - Write down the authors' @ handles and follow their postings
★ Website/Newsletter - Note web addresses and sign up for their newsletters if the authors have one
★ Email - List their contact info if you have access to it
★ Other - Add notes about places they inhabit (such as conferences) where you could *naturally* connect in person

Primary Fellow Author Profile Chart

Download this chart and others from the workbook via: *Bit.ly/KAC_BrandAuthor_BookFiles*

AUTHOR	SOCIAL	NEWSLETTER	EMAIL	OTHER

SECTION 3: PRIMARY TARGET AUDIENCE
Summary of Decisions

Just as in **Section 2**, be sure to clean up your final charts by editing and perhaps adding or researching a few details you may have missed. Refine both the *5WHS+2 Master Sheet* for your *Primary Target Audience Profile* and the *Primary Fellow Authors Profile*. Make a full-size final "master" copy of both profiles and insert them here.

If you're keeping computer files, create a new document labeled "Section3_Decisions" and store it in the subfolder you created called "Working Notes."

THE 5WH+2 Graphic Organizer:

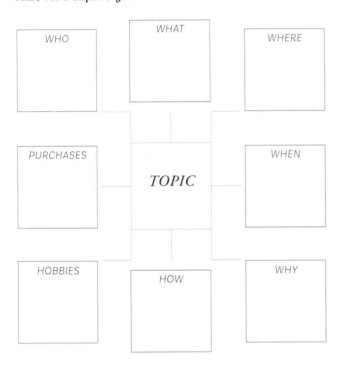

Primary Fellow Author Profile Chart

AUTHOR	SOCIAL	NEWSLETTER	EMAIL	OTHER

SECTION 4
PLATFORM TOOLS

(the gazebo and directional signs to it)

Time and money are precious resources for *Author Entrepreneurs*, and you don't want to waste either on platform tools that are ineffective.

To avoid Willy & Nilly, you need a methodical plan for selecting social media, collateral, and other materials. Thankfully, because you've completed Sections 1, 2, and 3* of this workbook, you have the means for intelligently building this part of your plan.

In this section, you'll:

STUDY/LEARN THE AUTHOR'S MARKETING FUNNEL &
CREATE A PRIORITIZED CHECK LIST OF THE TOOLS YOU'LL NEED

*If you've not completed these sections, doing this new one will be impossible. Go back and meet me here when you're ready.

Author's Marketing Funnel

Selecting your ideal author platform tools and prioritizing when to make them is easier when you understand the marketing funnel. The funnel, as illustrated by this not-so-fancy **Author Funnel** graphic below, is the order in which the majority of readers will discover you and engage with your platform tools. Let's break it down from the top...

The Author Funnel

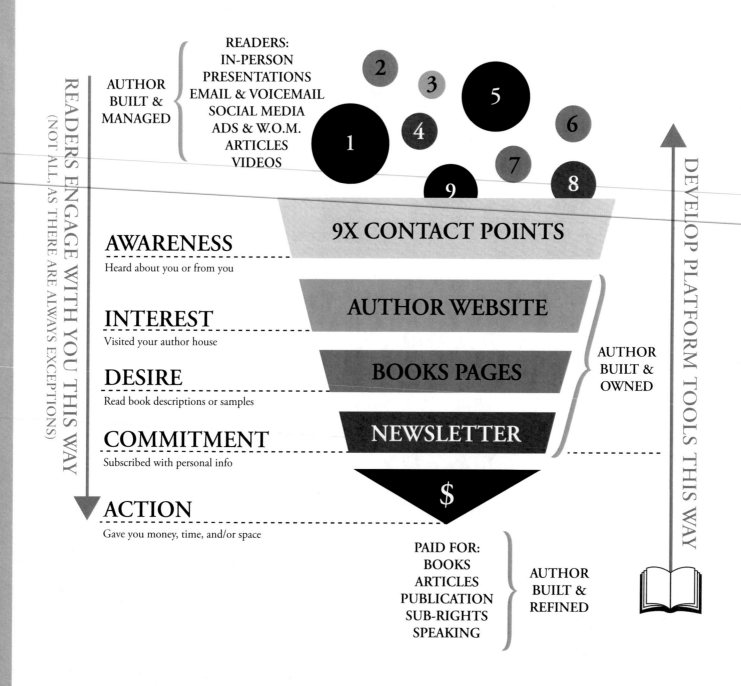

The Top Level of the Funnel and 9X Contact Points

It's generally believed, in marketing, it takes up to nine points of contact for a consumer to secure brand recognition, hand over cash, and/or become a loyal customer. Up to!

For any product or service including books, the nine times (9X) rule doesn't always apply. A book recommendation from a close friend can lead directly to a sale—just 1X. Some folks might engage with you 10X and still never buy a book. (What is wrong with those people?!)

Most of the 9X engagement happens at the top of the funnel. This top layer brings in consumers, drives them downward into the funnel, and includes vehicles such as:
★ Social Media
★ Print Collateral (Business cards, Bookmarks)
★ Video & Audio (YouTube, Podcasts)
★ Book Launches
★ Author Pages (Amazon, Goodreads)
★ Advertising
★ Publicity/Articles
★ Events and Presentation Materials
★ Word of Mouth/Recommendations

Don't fear the 9X rule, because the engagement-moments can add up quickly.

Let's say you give an author talk, use a PowerPoint presentation, and hand out business cards and bookmarks. You + the presentation slides + cards + bookmarks = 4X.

If attendees pop onto your website and sign up for your newsletter, they receive a confirmation email plus one newsletter. Now you're at 7X. If that emailed newsletter has a link to your Facebook page, which those attendees visit, and then you respond to any comments made with something witty and memorable—*boom*, you're at 9X. They won't likely forget you now.

Remember, consumers use *all* their senses to engage with a brand 9X. That means your readers might be able to touch, smell, hold, hear, or even taste your brand message and materials. Make that possible!

The Middle of the Funnel

The three most important and stabilizing supports for that 9X top-level experience are these three author-built and author-owned platform tools in the middle levels of that funnel:
★ Your website
★ Book pages (on your site and with online retailers)
★ Your newsletter + subscriber page

Why This Level Matters Most

Think of these three components as your *author home* (or the gazebo referenced earlier). This home is *one hundred percent* yours to own and maintain. And it is ultimately where you want people to visit.

Regardless if you are independently or traditionally published, in effect, you *rent* space on social websites such as Facebook and even Goodreads. If those platforms ever die (because people agree they do, in fact, have better things to do than social media), you would lose all those followers.

With your website, however, you will still own that space along with all those newsletter subscriber email addresses you collect.

For traditionally published authors, a warning: Do not rely on your publisher to create or build these author websites. Some traditional publishers offer their new authors a web page and a subscribe form on *their* publisher's website. But know this: it's *their* web page and readers are signing up for *their* subscriber list. If your publisher merges with another, decides not to reprint, or you go somewhere else with your next book, all the growth you might have had with readers in that space is not yours to take with you. Build your own website and author newsletter.

What You Want Readers to Do
As in any home, you want visitors to take off their shoes (in Canada, anyway). Linger. Curl up with a book. As readers navigate into and through your author house, they should feel welcome enough to hand over personal information—specifically, their email addresses. They will do so if they have the opportunity to:
★ Learn more about you and your books
★ Connect with you about talks and/or book clubs
★ Determine where to purchase your books

To be inviting, you need a minimum of five web pages, listed in the following *Tidbit*.

Tidbit AUTHOR WEBSITE BASIC PAGES

5 Main Rooms/Pages: When readers enter your house, at minimum they should see these five rooms or pages:
★ HOME: Includes links to all your social accounts, introductory info, and your latest book
★ ABOUT: Your author bio or *About the Author* section
★ BOOKS: A showcase of each of your titles with purchase links
★ NEWS: A newsletter sign-up page that describes what you share and how frequently
★ CONTACT: A form and/or email to contact you for talks, book clubs, or just because a reader adores you

Add-On Rooms: As you grow (or depending on how you engage with readers now), you might want additional rooms in your author house. I suggest you start simply with the five pages above. Remember, everything you build requires maintenance. Make those pages work for you before adding other rooms/pages such as:
★ Events listing. If you have only a few events a month, provide a list rather than a block-calendar.
★ Blog. Consistent posting with keywords can help with SEO, but a blog *does not* take the place of your e-mailed newsletter.
★ Book club information
★ Specifics about your presentation topics
★ Press coverage, especially if you write articles supporting nonfiction topics
★ Press kit with info about your book(s) and downloadable graphics and author headshots
★ Audio or video bells and whistles, and additional social media feeds

The Bottom of the Funnel

This spot—the one with the big dollar sign—is where you want readers, event coordinators, and fans to take action. Buying a book isn't the only outcome you want here. You want to be paid for your craft, yes, and so this dollar sign can also mean securing a presentation, visiting a book club, writing an article, and other gigs for which you hope to receive moolah. It might include ghost-writing, adapting a short story to stage or screen, or even finding funding or fellowships to work on your next book. If you look back at **Section 2: Author Message** and your word salad, you'll see you've already listed the paid gigs you hope to get.

Funnel Flow and Prioritizing Tool Creation

Readers tend to move through the marketing funnel from the top down (see the left-hand arrow). To guide them, your materials need to direct them on that downward journey from awareness through interest, desire, commitment, and ultimately to action.

But because their journey is downward, you need to build your tools in the opposite direction (right-hand arrow). Why? Here's an analogy.

No doubt you've seen a new restaurant open near you—the one that hung a cheap vinyl banner out front rather than taking an extra two weeks to get a branded, gorgeous sign. Perhaps you tried to Google the restaurant to find a website or reviews but found none. I'm pretty sure you wondered if maybe the food was as bad as the restaurant's presentation. Perhaps not consciously, but if you had a choice between vinyl-banner-café and gorgeous-signage café, you'd try the latter. That first impression is everything in marketing.

It's the same process for readers who connect with authors. If your website isn't completed and you post a picture of your cat admiring your new book on Instagram, the reader who loves your post has no *author home* to go to. If there isn't even a link in your bio, you'll likely lose a potential fan. It's far worse if they find your webpage "under construction."

Consequently, all your platform tools need to be built (or redesigned) from the bottom up *before* you show any of them to readers. This lets you build and then review all your elements. Your goal is to ensure your readers will have a consistent experience through every facet of your materials—from top to bottom of this funnel.

Tidbit WHEN DO YOU BUILD PLATORM TOOLS?

I'm sure your natural inclination is to wait until you've finished writing the book, and this isn't best for your brand. Build your platform tools and subscriber list NOW *while you write your first book*. Authors who launch their first book with 1000 fans and subscribers will be more successful more quickly. The earliest investors in your subscriber list are typically the most loyal and dedicated fans.

But don't take my word for it. Instead, read an original article by Kevin Kelly, founder of *Wired Magazine*, titled *1000 True Fans*: bit.ly/KAC_BrandAuthor5

I also appreciate this article by Navid Moazzez for its practical advice (including building a unique and authentic brand) for growing your true fan base: bit.ly/KAC_BrandAuthor6

Platform Tool Selection & Priorities

Okay, that was a *ton* of information on the marketing funnel. I'm sure you're wondering how you actually choose the platform tools you need. And how do you then create a priority list of what to create first? Well, this is a workbook after all, and your goal is to create a clear PLAN of what tools to build and when.

So let's do it.

STEP 1:
REVIEW YOUR PREVIOUS DECISIONS

All the beautiful decisions you made in the previous three sections will be applied in this step. Now is the time to go back and review your decisions for these pieces:

* ★ *SECTION 1: Time and Schedules*
* ★ *SECTION 1: Tasks and Competencies*
* ★ *SECTION 2: Author Message Paragraph*
* ★ *SECTION 3: Target Audience—Primary Readers & Fellow Authors Profiles*

STEP 2:
DOWNLOAD THE PLATFORM PRIORITY SPREADSHEET

Even if you don't like spreadsheets, one of the great benefits of this workbook is the **Platform Priority Spreadsheet**. And I've already created it for you (lucky you). I've posted this spreadsheet as an Excel document on my website, free for you to download. The next page has a sample you can use for referral, but to download the spreadsheet for free go to:

Bit.ly/KAC_BrandAuthor_BookFiles

If you are keeping "Working Notes" on your computer, download the spreadsheet to that same folder and label it "Section4_PlatformPrioritySpreadsheet." You will no doubt make several revisions to it before you have completed this section.

STEP 3:
FILLING IN THE PLATFORM PRIORITY SPREADSHEET

You'll see the platform tools on the spreadsheet are already prioritized. I've listed the tools in the order in which they should be created—in the *opposite* direction your readers will take through your marketing funnel. I urge you to keep this order intact and begin working with the spreadsheet as it is. From there, make the simplest decisions about what to build.

Because every brand is different, it's up to you to add, subtract, or revise the tools on this spreadsheet as you see fit. On the PDF you download, you'll see these colors:

* ★ *Orange headers* = the major platform tools
* ★ *Green headers* = the sub projects within those platform tools

You'll also see I've included some specific tasks, notes, and more. Next, let's look at those spreadsheet columns you will fill in.

Column A:
To Build (or Not to Build)

You'll see some are already labeled "YES!" They are a must for creating your author brand. These are the *author house* pieces (your gazebo) from the middle levels of the marketing funnel.

Beyond the basics, the rookie author might just check all the boxes. But not you. You do not need every little thing on this spreadsheet. How do you know? Because you've reviewed your decisions from **Section 3: Target Audience—Primary Readers** and **Fellow Authors Profiles**.

In the graphic organizer, and in the list of places your readers and fellow authors hang out, is the answer to which platform tools you will build.

★ If your readers do not hang out in Facebook, do not put an X in Column A next to Facebook.
★ If your fans are podcast junkies, you'll want an X next to Podcast.
★ Are you the keynote presenter at the next ComicCon? You might put an X next to Power Point presentation under "collateral."

Your decisions can be further informed by your **Section 2: Author Message**. Are the tools you are agreeing to build going to support that author message *authentically*?

Complete this column before moving on.

Columns D & E: By Vendor or By Me

Remember that task-assignment list you made in **Section 1: Tasks and Competencies**? Your *skills* and *joy* informed which tasks would be done by "H" for hired help, and which would be done by you, "O" for owner. That knowledge should help you realistically fill in these two columns. If, like me, you suck at programming and have zero desire to do it, you will need to hire a programmer. So you'll put an X in the "H=By Vendor" column for that task. If you have a programmer, you can put the person's actual name in that column.

Complete columns D & E before moving on.

Columns G & H: Estimates and Build-By Dates

Every author wants to know how much time and money it will take to get all this stuff done. And you've probably heard the answer, "It depends." It does, but let's try to qualify that statement.

The investment you make in building this brand and marketing for your *Author Entrepreneur* business depends on the commitments you made in **Section 1: Getting Yourself Organized** about schedules and competencies.

For example, if your marketing time will be only an hour a week and you're taking on the bulk of the branding tasks (checking Column E, "O = By Me") to lower your costs, it will take you longer to produce your platform tools than if you hired help. If your marketing hours are low but you intend to hire out all the work, your brand launch schedule might accelerate if you hire professionals and pay them accordingly.*

Generally speaking, your time and money schedule depends on this formula:

$$O + [H \times \$] \text{ affects } T$$

OWNER TIME (O)   HIRED HELP (H)
INVESTMENT ($)   SCHEDULE/TIME (T)

★ If you decrease O, H, and $, you'll have a longer production schedule (T)
★ If you decrease O, but increase H and $, you might shorten the schedule (T).
★ If you increase O, H, and $, you will significantly shorten the schedule (T).

Only you can make the decisions about time and money. Remember, a writing career is a long-term investment—a marathon, not a race. The intelligent tortoise wins in the long run. But you must make decisions based on your household income and expenses, realistic schedules, and how badly you want this writing business to thrive.

*Not in this or any other circumstances in life does throwing more money at a problem guarantee it will be solved quicker. The skill level of those you hire plus communication, weather, and human foibles all play a role.

The Platform Priority Spreadsheet

Download this chart and others from the workbook via: **Bit.ly/KAC_BrandAuthor_BookFiles**

TO BUILD	MAJOR PLATFORM TOOL / AUTHOR BRAND ELEMENTS	SPECIFIC TASK	H = BY VENDOR	O = BY ME	NOTES/SUGGESTIONS	ESTIMATE?	BUILD BY DATE	DONE!!
YES!	AUTHOR BRAND ELEMENTS				Same designer does elements & website.			
YES!		Logo			Not necessary. Some authors want one.			
YES!		Font Selection			No more than 2-3			
YES!		Color Selection			No more than 3-4			
YES!		Imagery Style (mood board)			Can make this on pinterest: http://bit.ly/KACChaseMoodBoard			
		Author Photoshoot			Hire a professional. On location? 3 Horiz & 3 Vertical			
YES!	NEWSLETTER				Set-up with MailChimp (built for and with website)			
		Define Messaging & Content Sections			Have 3. Your books. Your topics. + One more...			
		Set Mailing Schedule			Once a month minimum. More during book launches.			
		Get a Post-Office Box			MailChimp requires an address. Don't use your home.			
		Setup MailChimp Account			Free until 2500 followers			
		Create Newsletter Template			Make it & hold it until you have a handful of followers			
		Create a Physical Sign-up Sheet			You'll pass these out on a clipboard at in-person talks			
	Maintenance	Establish Ongoing Plan			Who will maintain this? You or an author assistant?			
YES!	BOOK PAGES				Same designer does elements & website.			
		Build Keyword List for Each Book			https://kindlepreneur.com/how-to-choose-kindle-keywords/			
		Build Book Descriptions w/ keywords or Work In Progress Description						
YES!	WEBSITE				Same designer does elements & website.			
		Buy Recommended URLs			Suggested BlueHost.com, but make sure you own it			
		Set Author Email for site			firstname@websiteURL.com + info@websiteURL.com			
		Write content for Pages			Mln - Home-Bio-Books-Events-Contact-Newsletter			
		Select Stock or Other Imagery			Ensure you have rights to images: istock.com or Pond5.com			
		Define Philanthropy/Charities			You can add a "giving" tab on your site to match this			
		Connect to Newsletter Mailchimp			Sign-up form will submit info to Mailchimp			
		Add in Social Platform Links			In order to add, go build these now and add them in			
	Maintenance	Update as necessary			Who will maintain this? Update Events, with new books, etc.			
	SOCIAL MEDIA							
		Instagram - Content Categories			Minimum recommended. Add in others as you see fit.			
		Posting Plan			A Public/Business one. A Visual Platform.			
		Engagement Plan			What will you post? https://katooroy.com/insta_resources			
		Setup Profile and first posts			Bio is abbreviated from website			
		Twitter						
		Posting Plan			Stay in Your Topic/Genre Lane Here			
		Engagement Plan			Begin by following authors in your genre			
		Setup Profile and first posts			Bio is abbreviated from website			
		Facebook Author Business Page						
		Posting Plan			Older but can do paid ads & join groups			
		Engagement Plan						
		Setup Profile and first posts			Bio is abbreviated from website			
		Pinterest						
		Posting Plan			Had a personal account? Will this be book related?			
		Engagement Plan						
		Setup Profile and first posts						
		Linked In						
		Adjust bio, photo, & writing/job info			Have one? Update your profile to include your author life			
		TikTok						
		Bio, photo, & create video campaign			Have one? Update your profile to include your author life			
	Maintenance	Establish for all above selected			Who will do this? You or an author assistant?			
	AMAZON CENTRAL				You Own This & Claim Your Books			
		Setup Author Profile			https://authorcentral.amazon.com/gp/help			
		Add bio to match website bio			Slightly modify to ensure your website is in the first 3 lines			

GOODREADS AUTHOR
You Own This & Claim Your Books

- Setup Author Profile — https://www.goodreads.com/author/program
- Add bio to match website bio — Slightly modify to ensure your website is in the first 3 lines
- Add new author photo
- Claim your book titles
- Add any videos or book trailers

(also listed: Add new author photo · Claim your book titles · Add any videos or book trailers · Link if you have a blog)

COLLATERAL/OTHER/TALKS
To Connect with Readers & Speaking Venues

- **YES!** Business Cards — Min of website and info@ email address (no book covers)
- Book Marks/Stickers — Different from bus. cards + list your website
- PowerPoint Presentation Templates — Website link on Every Slide

VIDEO & AUDIO OPTIONS

YOUTUBE
- Determine Content Purpose
- Posting Plan
- Engagement Plan
- Editor or Production Coordination
- Build First Videos
- Setup Profile and first posts

PODCAST
- Determine Your Theme
- Build Logo & Season Outline
- Write Scripts or Build Interview Lineup
- Establish Recording Options

Not about writing. What topic could your brand really own?

Book Trailers
- About Book or Author Interview?
- Editor or Production Coordination

OTHER MARKETING BITS

AUTHOR BRAND LAUNCH
Redifine/Expand these with their own priority lists

- **YES!** Launch Website First
- **YES!** Make all Social Platforms Live
- **YES!** Email Outreach for Newsletter — Individual emails to ask your closest friends to join
- **YES!** Post on Social re: Brand & Signup — Posts with a sign-up link (no spamming)
- Email Agent & Publisher — Send links & ask to update books, bio & all book pages
- Press Kit (Page on website or PDF) — If done by Agent/Publisher, redo it to match your brand

BOOK LAUNCHES
- PreOrder Giveaways
- Special Newsletter Giveaways
- Build Street Team
- Plan a heck of a Party

PUBLICITY & ARTICLES
- Submit News to Literary Organizations
- Outreach for articles or contributions
- Outreach for blog/newsletter Tours
- Outreach for speaking engagements

ADVERTISING
Can be costly, so use/build your own platform tools first

- Amazon Ad Campaigns — Only for self-pub authors
- Facebook Ad Campaigns — Self or Trad Authors can run there
- Web & Gif Ads — Run on other people's newsletters or Websites
- Magazine or Other Ads
- From the Publisher Graphics — These are for Amazon Book Pages

DEVELOPED BY KARENACHASE.COM

Who's the boss? Oh, yeah, that's you!!

(And sometimes Tony Danza.)

Remember, though, this is a business, and you are the BOSS of it. Take time to become informed, be practical, and build a simple and practical plan and budget to support your endeavors.

How to Gather Estimates

Going back to the spreadsheet, for every X in the "H=By Vendor" column, you'll need to conduct research for local or remote talent and then get estimates for completing each task.

I can tell you, I've seen authors launch a terrific website for only a few hundred dollars. And I've worked with clients who spent between $1500 and $7000, depending on how much we created from scratch and what their reach and goals were.

Some things to keep in mind:

★ Items listed in the spreadsheet in rows 1–35 are best done together, by one designer, to improve consistency.

★ Choose wisely; there are professional brand designers and there are "my son in our basement" designers.

★ Ask authors you know for vendor recommendations and trust their opinions.

★ Locate branding and design university programs with students who need work for their portfolios. This is a good option for beginning authors and those on a tight budget.

★ Local talent can meet with you in person, but if readers are remote, why not your vendors?

★ Get three estimates for each project and consider more than just the cheapest one. Talent, time, and references may all play a role.

Set Realistic Build-By Dates

As you gather estimates, your vendors will ask, "When do you want this?" Before you get those estimates, put together a practical schedule based on your life and publishing goals. What is realistic?

With the majority of my clients, I've found it takes three to six months to build their platform tools and launch their brands. That is little time to invest in a long-term writing career, considering some authors spend two years in an MFA program.

If you have a book launch date, I recommend planning to launch your brand at least three months before that day. You'll need the time to build a newsletter subscriber list and capture all the new readers you'll get on day one.

If you don't have a book coming out anytime soon, you have the luxury of stretching this out based on your budget and the hours for marketing each week. However, working within a six- to twelve-month timeframe can allow you to maintain focus so projects don't linger into obscurity.

Humans tend to work better under deadlines. Setting a schedule gives you goals to strive for, but go easy on yourself. This entrepreneurial adventure is supposed to be a joy, not a forced march.

Take your time with your Platform Priority Spreadsheet.

It's a crucial piece to your Final Brand Plan.

A Word on Book Pages on Websites

If you do not yet have a book completed (and you are a good soldier, building an author brand before your book is even finished), you might still create a BOOK page on your website.

While keywords and final book description might need to wait, you'll write a general description about the topic of your work in progress. When your book is getting closer to publication, then you'll come back and flesh out the page.

Tidbit WHO WILL STEAL YOUR IDEAS?

I know of authors who freak out and say, "If I share my book idea, someone will steal it and write the book before I do!" I can't guarantee this won't happen, but I can guarantee one thing. The general population is too lazy or too overwhelmed in their own lives to write the book you're writing. And most authors have book ideas they're already working on, so they're not likely to drop their ideas to steal yours.

When it comes to your writing, Malcolm Gladwell's advice is not to worry about theft. Instead, share what you're writing with every person willing to listen, even for a few seconds. Those people just might do or say something that will improve your project.

I highly recommend Gladwell's MasterClass on writing (even if you don't write nonfiction). For this and other writing-related Master Classes: Bit.ly/KAC_BrandAuthor7

SECTION 4: PLATFORM TOOLS
Summary of Decisions

There comes a time when, even with spreadsheets, you must stop working on them and instead use them as a tool to get projects completed.

Before you move on to **Section 5: Brand Elements**, take your finest version of the **Platform Priority Spreadsheet** and move it into the computer subfolder you created (way back in **Step 1**) called "Platform Tool Plan." This will be a functioning, editable plan you can use going forward.

Nicely done, you.
You've worked hard to get here.

And you probably need a break.

Go watch a movie. Grab a cocoa (or something stronger) and I'll meet you in the next section in a few days when you're no longer thinking about spreadsheets.

———

THE BICYCLE WAS CREATED AFTER THE WHEEL PROVED USEFUL.

———

KEEPING TOOLS SIMPLE IN THE BEGINNING MEANS THERE IS LESS TO MAINTAIN & MORE TIME TO WRITE

SECTION 5
BRAND ELEMENTS

(the gazebo they see and experience)

What you have from the previous four sections is a lot of words. However, a brand made up of words and sentences doesn't help trigger memories for the consumers of that brand. Visuals do.

So, let's go back to your words from Sections 1–4 and define the visuals. These parameters will become your author brand elements guidelines.

In this section, you'll make decisions about:

*FONTS, COLORS, IMAGERY OR PHOTOS, AND THE STYLE OF YOUR BRAND**

*This "fun stuff" is often where writers like to begin. They want to skip over all that good thinking and planning and just pick their favorite colors. NO!

If you've skimmed this workbook and want to begin here, I beg you… just walk away and get a snack. You're likely hungry and not thinking clearly. When you come back, start at the beginning and complete the sections in the order discussed. Pleeeease. (Heavens, there's always that *one* student…)

Author Brand Elements

There are thousands of fonts, colors, and photos styles are available, which results in billions of combinations. So how do you freakin' choose? You don't.

You follow a logical three-step path to narrowing down the options. This ensures your brand elements speak to your target audience, while also meeting the criteria of being consistently, uniquely, and authentically you.

STEP ONE: STUDY YOUR FELLOW AUTHORS

Looking back at **Section 3: Target Audience**, pull up the websites of three or four of the authors you listed as cooperative or complementary. You previously studied them for platform tool ideas; now you'll study the look and feel of their brand elements through their websites. Why?

You need to look like you belong in that crowd,
and you need to stand out from that crowd.

If this sounds like I'm now asking you to look at them as "comparative," in this instance, yep, I am. What authors *look* like to readers is different from how you need to view working with authors. So, for each author, list the person's website URL and then write down words about the colors, fonts, imagery, photography, and style you see.

Example: Let's again look at Victorian/Historical Crime Thrillers author, Bradley Harper. He's at BHarperAuthor.com, ad his brand can be described thusly:

★ Fonts: Script and two other fonts. One clean (sans serif). One standard text (serif).
★ Colors: Grey, red, and brown
★ Imagery: Black and white images. Maps. Sepia-toned antique photos. Textured papers.
★ Photos: Black and white. Kind of like Sherlock Holmes at an historic outdoor location.
★ Style: Masculine yet Victorian. Moody but with splashes of (appropriately) blood red.

YOU'RE ALSO THE BOSS OF HOW
YOU LOOK. YOU MAKE THE DRESS
CODE FOR YOUR AUTHOR LIFE.

STEP 1A:
FILL IN THE FELLOW AUTHOR BRAND ELEMENTS CHART

Using the chart below, fill in descriptions for up to four of your fellow authors.

AUTHOR NAME/WEBSITE	FONTS	COLORS	IMAGERY	PHOTO	STYLE

STEP 1B:
ASSESS THE SIMILARITIES
IN ELEMENTS OF FELLOW AUTHORS

Looking at that chart, it's time to assess if there are consistencies and patterns in what you wrote. Why? If ALL your fellow authors use blue, you might fit in by also using blue but you risk looking like everyone else. Worse, blue might be the least appropriate color to describe you.

Transfer the top one or two "consistencies list" here:

FONTS	COLORS	IMAGERY	PHOTO	STYLE

STEP 1C:
CATALOG YOUR FAVORITE AND LEAST FAVORITE ELEMENTS OF YOUR FELLOW AUTHORS

Look at the **Step 1A fellow author chart** again, plus your consistencies chart. Now from those two charts, enter *your* top preferences here, and then rate them as LOVE or LIKE.

FONTS	COLORS	IMAGERY	PHOTO	STYLE	PREFERENCE
					LOVE — LIKE
					LOVE — LIKE
					LOVE — LIKE
					LOVE — LIKE
					LOVE — LIKE

*Before we use these charts to pick your colors,
let's take a little journey together—into your bedroom
and specifically into your closet.*

STEP TWO: STUDY YOURSELF

The task is to define you—the main character in your branding story. Just as writers use clothes, shoes, and jewelry to define their protagonists, what you wear also says a lot about your style, image, and personality.

Next time you're at a writer's conference, take a look at the attendees. There's the mod-man who wears nothing but neutral colors in cotton or linen. There's the dude in the band t-shirt talking with that hip lady in her bohemian dress. And note the big difference between the woman wearing Armani heels and the chick wearing Lands End hiking boots.

Those people (characters) are all displaying their unique brand elements.

So, what's in your closet or dresser?

I'm not talking about your Saturday schlumpy yoga pants with the Cheeto® stains you won't let anyone but your family see. Instead, think about those clothes you'll wear to an author presentation or writing conference. (If you've never thought about your clothes at all, or you only wear Cheeto-stained sweats in public, well... is that image authentic to your brand?)

Describe your clothes, shoes, and accessories by color:

Describe your clothes, shoes, and accessories by fabric:

Describe your clothes, shoes, and accessories by style:

List the brands, if any, you tend to buy:

Describe how you feel in your clothes:

```

```

Flip back to the *Word Salad* you made in **Section 2: Author Message**. Pull out the words related to personality (described by you and your family/friends) and put them here:

_____   _____   _____

_____   _____   _____

_____   _____   _____

STEP THREE: YOUR BRAND ELEMENT GUIDELINES

Reviewing all the words you've written in the charts and lists from **Steps 1 and 2** above, you likely see consistencies and coordinating imagery.* For each of the categories below, write in your three preferences. Just three! Based on the work you've just done, they should be your favorite selections, ones that are most authentically you. These, then, are your brand elements.*

My Brand Elements Might Include:

FONTS	COLORS	IMAGERY	PHOTO	STYLE

To make this a truly visual exercise, you can use Pinterest and create a "mood board" for your author brand. You can see my author brand mood board here:
★ Pinterest Link: bit.ly/KAC_BrandAuthor8
And if you visit my website, you can see how that mood board influenced the final brand:
★ KarenAChase.com

* Gosh, let's hope so. If it's total chaos, or you're really at a loss, please seek outside viewpoints here. Your spouse might be dying to give you an opinion about those sweatpants.

Tidbit THREE MAIN FONT CATEGORIES

SERIF: These have little decorative stems (called serifs) that stick out from the tips, bottom, or tops of each letter. The letters have fatter and thinner sections, rather than being even all the way around. Times New Roman, Palatino, and Garamond are three examples of serif type often used in books.

This text is a serif font (Adobe Garamond).

SANS SERIF: *Sans* is French for without, as in no serifs. Most sans serif fonts have evenly constructed letters—no thick-to-thin stems. Helvetica, Arial, and Avenir are three common examples.

This text is a sans serif font (Basic).

SCRIPT: These fonts look like they are created by hand or with a calligraphy pen. It's not great for long-form paragraphs because the thick-to-thin script fonts are difficult to read—especially for youngsters who've not learned cursive (curses!)—but it can add a flourish to headings.

This text a script font (Good Vibrations).

These are the three main categories, however there are dozens of display and decorative fonts that look like kid handwriting, roman engravings, or even the wild, wild west. Woah. Go easy with these, Trigger. Unique fonts can drive a brand to look special, but it's a short road to cheesy and awful. Comic sans comes to mind. (To learn why, Google: "Comic sans sucks.")

Tidbit DEFINE YOUR STYLE A LA HEPBURN

When it comes to choosing brand elements—fonts, colors, imagery, and more—classic is more enduring than following a fad. Choose only what is hot-right-now and tomorrow you might end up looking like yesterday.

My advice is to think like Katharine Hepburn. Because she simplified and chose what was authentic to her, all these years later, we have a memorable picture of who she was (and who she wasn't). She explains her style in two quotes:

"I wear my sort of clothes to save me the trouble of deciding which clothes to wear."

"If you always do what interests you, at least one person is pleased."

SECTION 5: BRAND ELEMENTS
Summary of Decisions

It's so easy to play with colors and fonts until the cows come home, but it's time to *mooove* on. Besides, I think you have a book or two to write and publish.

It's time to commit to your brand elements here. Notice the word "might" is still in the heading for this chart. In **PART III: POST-BRAND PLANNING**, we'll talk about how to work with a professional to ensure these elements are ready for print and web design. Their input can help modify these slightly in order to make the brand better coordinated and easier to build for the long-term.

My Brand Elements Might Include:

FONTS	COLORS	IMAGERY	PHOTO	STYLE

If you've created a Pinterest mood board, insert the URL here:

_____

THERE IS NO LINE BETWEEN PERCEPTION & REALITY.

SO BEING REAL IS SIMPLY BETTER FOR YOUR BRAND

SECTION 6
YOUR FINAL BRAND PLAN

Congratulations!
You've made it through the five main sections.

Now is the time to finally (and fully) commit
to everything that has come before
this section and write out your:

FINAL BRAND PLAN

Final Brand Plan

Are you ready? Go...

STEP 1:
CREATE THE FINAL BRAND PLAN.DOCX

Remember that **Final Brand Plan** folder you created on your computer?
Open a new MSWord document and save it into that folder, labeled as:
YourName_FinalBrandPlan_TodaysDate.docx

STEP 2:
GATHER YOUR DECISIONS INTO ONE DOCUMENT

One-by-one, go back through your **Summary of Decisions** from **Sections 1–5** and type them into this document. The completed document, along with your **Platform Tools Priority list** (in Excel), gives you what this workbook promised:

A written plan that brands the author (not the book).

AN OPTION FOR THE HAND-WRITING MAVENS

If you're the type of person who wants it all in writing, on paper, and you want one last shot at refining (nit-picking) your verbiage and choices, then the next few pages in this print version are just for you. Here, you can copy the text from all of your **Summary of Decisions** from **Sections 1–5**.

YOU'RE SO CLOSE...

WHAT WILL YOU DO TO CELEBRATE HAVING A WRITTEN BRAND PLAN?

NAP? CHOCOLATE & TACOS?

MY FINAL BRAND PLAN
Summary of Decisions

SECTION 1:
GETTING ORGANIZED

DOCUMENT MAINTENANCE

My physical storage options for notes and documents is: _____
- ❑ I have set up folders on my computer.

My Author Entrepreneur office hours are:

_____ (days of the week)
_____ (hours per session)
Total: _____ (hours per week)

This makes my Author Entrepreneur hours:

No Book Yet:
Writing Hours (75%) _____ per week
Business Hours (25%) _____per week

Pre- & Post-Launch:
Writing Hours (25%) _____ per week
Business Hours (75%) _____ per week

Launch Month:
Writing Hours (0%) _____ per week
Business Hours (100%) _____ per week

My Writing Hours will generally be at:
_____ (this day/time)
My Business Hours will generally be at:
_____ (this day/time)
My holidays/vacations will be: _____

_____

_____

Tasks and Competencies
- ❑ Evaluated my SKILL level
- ❑ Evaluated my JOY level
- ❑ Assigned tasks to owner (O) or to help (H) as noted below:

TASK	Assigned to
Advertising Development	
Copywriting	
Event Planning	
Illustration	
Newsletter Development	
Newsletter e-Mailings	
Photography	
Power Point Development	
Print Design	
Print Production (Printing)	
Publicity/Press Releases	
Scheduling Events	
Social Media Development	
Social Media Posts/Updates	
Web Design	
Web Programming	
Other:	

SECTION 2:
AUTHOR MESSAGE

SECTION 4:
PLATFORM TOOLS & PRIORITIES

THE 5WH+2 Graphic Organizer:

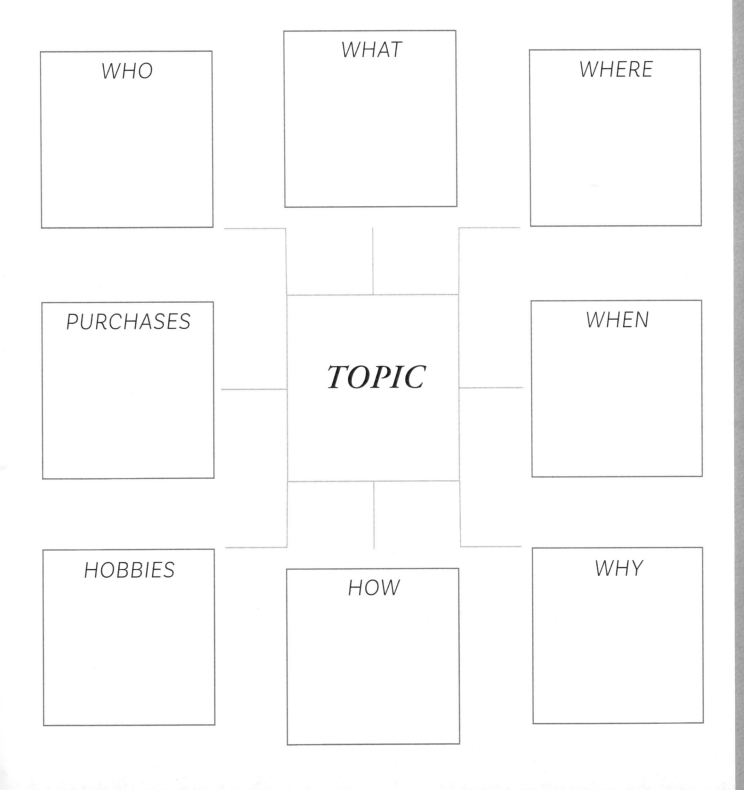

Primary Fellow Author Profile Chart

AUTHOR	SOCIAL	NEWSLETTER	EMAIL	OTHER

SECTION 4:
PLATFORM TOOLS & PRIORITIES

❑ I have selected and prioritized what I will need for my brand, and the **Platform Priority Spreadsheet** is in my the computer subfolder I created (way back in **Step 1**) called "Platform Tool Plan."

SECTION 5:
BRAND ELEMENTS

My Brand Elements Might Include:

FONTS	COLORS	IMAGERY	PHOTO	STYLE

My Pinterest mood board (if I created one), can be found at the URL here:

_____

SECTION 6:
MY FINAL BRAND PLAN

❑ I have gathered all my summary information here and/or on my computer.

SECTION 6: FINAL BRAND PLAN
Summary of Decisions

Look at all your hard work! Very few authors have written brand plans, but not you! Not only do you have that brand plan, I'm sure you have a clearer picture of who you are as an author, who your readers are, and you have a list of tools to make in order to connect with them.

I'm totally proud of you!
Nicely done, Boss.

Pat yourself on the back and lift a glass of champagne or go get that well-earned chocolate or taco (or both). After a sufficient break, please join me back here, and reread this quote by J.W. (Bill) Marriott, from the beginning of the workbook.

"Once you decide to decide,
life becomes very simple.

You don't have to think about certain
issues or questions again.

You simply get on with things."

You've made so many decisions, and so now it's time to act, to simply get on with enacting your plan so your brand can come to fruition.

The next step is to get all those platform tools developed in a logical order. I'm not going to leave you all alone to work on it quite yet. Instead, you'll find several tips in **PART III: POST-BRAND PLANNING** to help you get to work.

LEAN IN TO THE BRAND YOU ARE!

GET READY, GET SET PREPARE TO LAUNCH YOUR BRAND & CAREER

Plan? Yes. Now, enact!

Building a brand is accomplished the same
way a writer becomes an author...
by being persistent and seeing your plans
through to the end.

PART III

*WHAT NOW?
POST-BRAND
PLANNING*

Post-Brand Planning

You have this whole written plan, and you have your **Platform Tool Spreadsheet**, and now you likely want answers to these questions:
- ★ WHAT do you do with the plan you have in hand?
- ★ WHO sees it?
- ★ WHEN do you launch your new brand?
- ★ HOW often do you update your brand plan?

WHAT:
START AT THE TOP
AND SEEK OUTSIDE HELP.

Start at the top of your **Platform Tool Spreadsheet** and work your way down. Remember in **Section 1: Tasks and Competencies** how you defined your skills, and you were also honest about where you have none?

If you're not a professional designer, finding one should be your first step. Refer to the tips about gathering estimates in **Section 4: Platform Tools**.

A designer will help translate your list of fonts, colors, and imagery into actual font names and well-defined colors consistent for print and web. Getting a professional photographer lined up will help provide the author photos for all the tools you'll build.

WHO:
SHARE YOUR PLAN.

For any professionals who work with you, sharing your written **Final Brand Plan** is essential. Every vendor you hire—designer, photographer, publicist, etc.—should be adhering to *your* standards and sharing *your* author message. If you created a mood board on Pinterest or by some other means, you should share that, too. *Everyone* needs to be creating your brand according to your plan.

WHEN:
TAKE YOUR TIME.

Brands are not built overnight. As discussed in **Section 4**, working your way down that **Platform Tool List**, may take months depending on your schedule. During that time, I encourage you to not update or modify your brand plan. Every time you do, everything has to shift to accommodate the change. Stay with your decisions and work on it consistently, even if it takes a while.

WHEN:
LAUNCH YOUR NEW
AUTHOR BRAND AND
PLATFORM TOOLS IN ONE GO.

As you work through your **Platform Priority Spreadsheet** of tasks, I urge you not to launch any of the pieces/tools until they're ALL ready to go—especially those elements in rows 1-35.

Your "author house" is your priority, yes, but having your social media and your podcast available will drive readers to those layers of your marketing funnel. Dribbling a new brand out in bits is also a missed opportunity for having fun with your own smashing publicity.

Set a launch date for your brand and platform tools and work backwards, adjusting that launch/production schedule as needed. Then sit back and enjoy your own show.

After it launches, your job is then to ensure you have a maintenance schedule. How will you update social posts, put together your newsletter, etc. Again, refer to your **Section 1: Tasks and Competencies** about whether or not that will be you. Having an intern or author assistant might be what you need to stay on task and *consistently* connect with readers.

HOW:
UPDATE YOUR
FINAL BRAND PLAN.

Your plan serves as a firm foundation that should endure for years to come. The *Shell* gas station colors are original to 1915, and the last time that logo was updated was 1971. That is the kind of consistency you're looking for.

Even little ol' me has had the same swirling pen logo for nearly twenty years—for both my design life and my author life—and I'm still operating with the author brand plan I wrote in 2018, with slight adjustments when it was necessary. For instance, when launching this workbook, my brand plan was revisited to ensure my messaging and tools were inclusive of this new publication for my readers. I will build specific campaigns for a book, but my author brand is as consistent as can be.

Advertising campaigns can change every year, but great brands endure.

Even if you need to redo your website in five years because of outdated operating systems or old author photos, your brand colors, fonts, and messaging will likely stay as they are now.

Your readers need time to see and recognize your brand through all those 9X moments and more. For some readers, it will take months or years to fall deeply in love with you. Keep your brand, messaging, and elements for a good long while, and you'll build a healthy relationship with readers.

So when *should* you tweak the brand plan to accommodate what is new? I recommend every year in February (the dullest of months), you read through your brand plan—refamiliarize yourself with your decisions and make minor tweaks only if necessary. You might consider updating your plan when/if you:

★ Produce books with drastically different genres/topics than you have now
★ Go through a major life change that affects your *Author Entrepreneur* life
★ Shift from writing part-time to full-time or vice versa
★ Get a major publishing or film deal that puts you on a different stage

Thankfully, if any of those things occur, you have in your hands a tool—this workbook—to help you refine your plan. Go through each section again with your old plan in hand. Update the **Final Brand Plan** and the **Platform Tools List** only where it no longer works for you. Hopefully you'll have some additional data about which platform tools have been best for you over time (and as social channels and publishing itself changes).

But for now, you've created a plan. You have a spreadsheet. And you've made a ton of decisions that are authentic, consistent, and unique to you.

I'm grateful you invested in your author brand with me.

Now, off you go, Boss. Have a grand time being yourself.

★ ★ ★

PS: Ongoing Brand Maintenance

The **Platform Tools Priority List** is really designed to help you *launch* a brand. However, in that spreadsheet you'll notice a few lines about "maintenance." Every single piece you build has to be updated—and those tasks fall into one of two categories.

Monthly Marketing & Communication Tasks

Part of your ongoing job—during those business hours you've set aside—is to maintain your author brand materials and stick to posting schedules for newsletters, blog, and social media. There are a multitude of folks—professionals and students—out there to help with those tasks. These include a category called "Author Assistants."

I found one to work with by putting out a Twitter call for support, but you'll also find legitimate freelancers working as Author Assistants. They charge by the hour or month, and typically work with you to help with those social media tasks. Mine even entered names into my newsletter subscriber list after every event.

Annual Updates to all Tools

When you make those February tweaks to your brand, or when you have grander changes, these maintenance updates to your tools can feel like a bear. Where do you begin to assess and make updates, and in what order?

Once again, here's a handy chart! Simply copy this checklist and every February go through it, in order. Let the compass be your guide as an acronym for the updates.
- ★ North = Newsletter
- ★ West = Website
- ★ East = Education
- ★ South = Social
- ★ Compass = Collateral
- ★ All Points = Advertising

HAVE FUN!

WRITING IS A JOB BUT IT AIN'T LIKE WE'RE ROOFIN' IN THE BLAZING SUMMER HEAT!

Download this chart and others from the workbook via: **Bit.ly/KAC_BrandAuthor_BookFiles**

BRAND PLATFORM TOOLS REVIEW & MAINTENANCE GUIDE

N	NEWSLETTER
W	WEBSITE
E	EDUCATION
S	SOCIAL
C	COLLATERAL
A	ADVERTISING

Let the Compass be your guide:

N

W   E

S

COMPASS ~ ALL POINTS

Notes:

NEWSLETTER
- ❑ Topics & schedule
- ❑ Giveaway plans
- ❑ Template
- ❑ Headers & imagery

WEBSITE
- ❑ Pop-up plans
- ❑ Homepage & slider
- ❑ Book pages
- ❑ Other subpages
- ❑ Bio/press kit page
- ❑ Contact page

EDUCATION
- ❑ Blog topics & tours
- ❑ Classes/speaking details
- ❑ Videos/youtube
- ❑ Book trailer/speaking reels

SOCIAL
- ❑ Instagram plan/posts updates
- ❑ FB twitter plan/post updates
- ❑ Book review posts
- ❑ Book sales posts
- ❑ Goodreads update

COLLATERAL
- ❑ Postcards updates/orders
- ❑ Book marks orders
- ❑ Business card orders
- ❑ Book mailing materials

ADVERTISING
- ❑ Magazine or print plans
- ❑ Online plans
- ❑ Press releases
- ❑ Other

…Still freaking out?

If you're really at a loss, and you need extra help, well… this whole branding thing is what I've done since 1994. (Yep, I'm that old.)

For those who have already given it their all with this workbook, I do offer hourly one-on-one brand planning sessions . I can also help you design and launch all those brand platform tools.

For author branding services, my portfolio samples, or to inquire about one-on-one hourly consultations visit my website:

KARENACHASE.COM

SCAN FOR SERVICES

A LITTLE BEGGING

If you feel empowered or launch an author brand using this workbook, I hope you'll share that information with friends but also online:

Tag @KarenAChase:
#AuthorBrandWorkbook
#BossofMyAuthorBusiness
#ImAnAuthorEntreprenuer

If you loved this book, or it helped you in some way, please buy a copy for a fellow author. I'd also appreciate a helpful review on Amazon and/or Goodreads. (She asked, shamelessly.)

KARENACHASE.COM

SCAN FOR INSTAGRAM

SEEK MORE INSPIRATION...

Branding, travel, photography, writing, entrepreneurship, and historical research...
I'm always eager to share great stories, the common thread between them all.

My blog, *Compositions*, touches on the events, places, writers, and artists that are thoughtfully adding to our collective American history. Guest posts are also welcomed and celebrated. Please contact me for details.

KARENACHASE.COM/BLOG

About Karen A. Chase

AUTHOR.
SPEAKER.
BRAND DESIGNER.

For nearly three decades Karen has worked as a professional designer creating brands for national and international organizations, non-profits, and authors. She launched 224Pages, her own publishing house in 2011. She's an engaging keynote speaker, presenting to audiences in the US and Canada—both virtually and in-person—about history, branding, and entrepreneurship. She's a long-standing member of the Daughters of the American Revolution, James River Writers, and the Historical Novelist Society. Originally from Calgary, Alberta, Canada, she now resides in Richmond, Virginia.

BOOKS

Bonjour 40: A Paris Travel Log
Her first book, this travel essay garnered seven independent publishing awards.

Carrying Independence
About the signing of the Declaration, the novel was awarded No. 12 on Shelf Unbound's Top 100 Indie Books of 2019.

Mary Angela's Kitchen
Published in 2021, it's a short foodie-based story, with four easy Italian recipes.

SIGN UP FOR MORE:

Subscribe to Karen's e-publication, *Chasing Histories*, featuring historical research, travel tips, branding anecdotes and advice, and author event details. Visit:

KARENACHASE.COM

SCAN TO SUBSCRIBE TO MY NEWSLETTER

With Thanks

Books are never made alone. Years of working with authors, companies, and nonprofits culminated into the wisdom (and maybe a bit of the sass) you now hold in your hand.

I also thank Barbara McNichol who took her mighty pen to my manuscript to ensure it was a book worthy of standing alongside those on business shelves.

A big thank you to Colleen Sheehan who took this heaping print book and made an equally effective ebook version.

While this book was going through production, the brilliant sisters Christina Reeser and Diana Mahmoud made my website portal far more robust to include this new book—they updated keywords, navigation, and so much more to better reflect my brand messaging. I am in awe of what you do.

To Leslie Saunderlin and Kris Spisak for providing design, business, writing, and just life advice. To all my early reviewers, and especially to Katharine Herndon. Your review—both funny and thoughtful—was like handing my conscience a freakin' red pen. Chocolate well-earned, my friend.

And of course, with love to Ted. My true author home is wherever you are.

Karen A. Chase

Build brands.
Make memories.
Scatter joy.

KARENACHASE.COM